SIMPLE MATH!

200 WORD PROBLEMS WITH ANSWERS | 3000+FACT WORKSHEETS

MULTIPLICATION & DIVISION

www.aceacademicpublishing.com

Author: Ace Academic Publishing

Prepaze is a sister company of Ace Academic Publishing. Intrigued by the unending possibilities of the internet and its role in education, Prepaze was created to spread the knowledge and learning across all corners of the world through an online platform. We equip ourselves with state-of-the-art technologies so that knowledge reaches the students through the quickest and the most effective channels.

The materials for our books are written by award winning teachers with several years of teaching experience. All our books are aligned with the state standards and are widely used by many schools throughout the country.

For enquiries and bulk order, contact us at the following address:

3736, Fallon Road, #403
Dublin, CA 94568
www.aceacademicpublishing.com

ISBN: 978-1-949383-34-8

PARENT'S GUIDE

This book is suitable for kids in the age range of 4-8. The book contains several pages of math fact tests that can be an excellent practice to increase fluency in basic math operations. Not only that, but the book also contains 200-word problems that can also help your student apply the facts that they have practiced. We always try to ensure that the kids have a fun learning experience and so we have also included several fun activities. This is an excellent book for your kids to practice facts, understand word problems, and have fun with them!

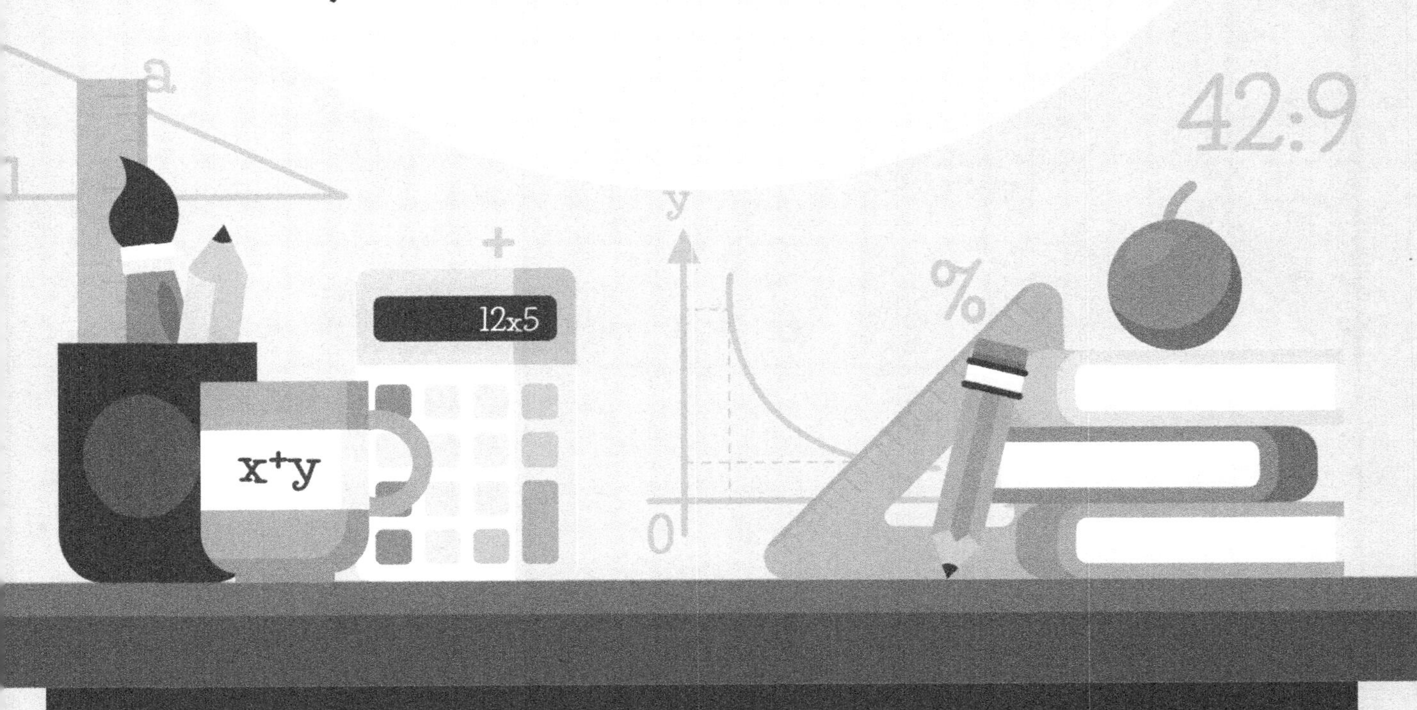

Other books from Ace Academic Publishing

TABLE OF CONTENTS

HELLO EVERYONE!

Let's learn math with

MULTIPLICATION

Shall we start?
Let's go!

MULTIPLICATION

The basic concept of **multiplication** operation is **repeated addition.**

In cases where a specific number is repeated over and again, we tend to add the same number to count the total number of entities. This long process can be simplified by the operation of multiplication.

The numbers that we multiply are called the **multiplicand** and the **multiplier** and the result is called the **product.** The operation is represented by the **cross** operator which is denoted similar to the letter **X** of the alphabet.

Example:

$2 + 2 + 2 = 2 \times 3 = 6$

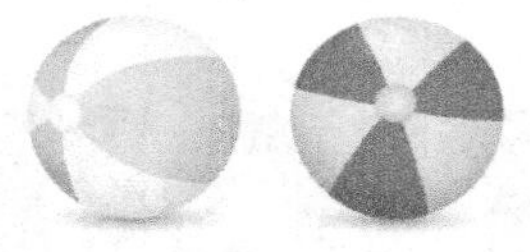 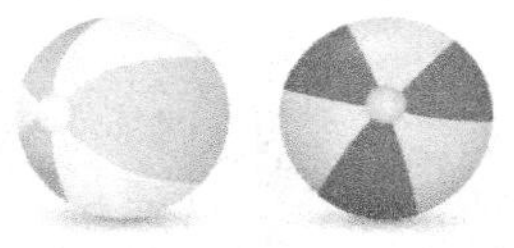 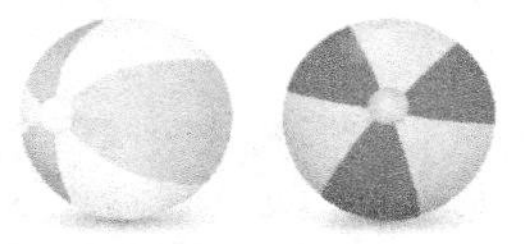

Here, 2 is the multiplicand, 3 is the multiplier and 6 is the product.

Also, $3 + 3 = 3 \times 2 = 6$

   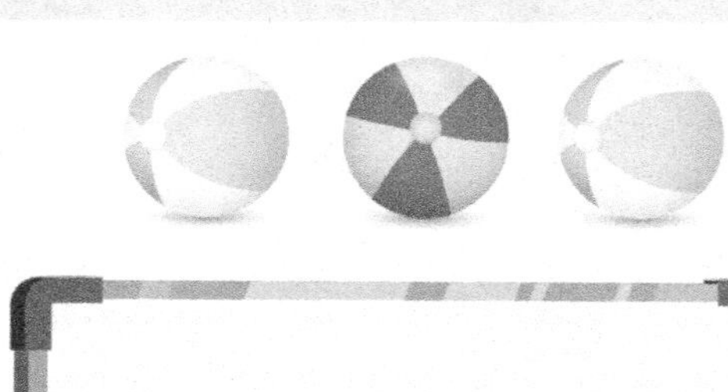

Here, 3 is the **multiplicand**, 2 is the **multiplier** and 6 is the **product**.

Note that, 2 x 3 = 6 and 3 x 2 = 6. Hence, 2 x 3 = 3 x 2

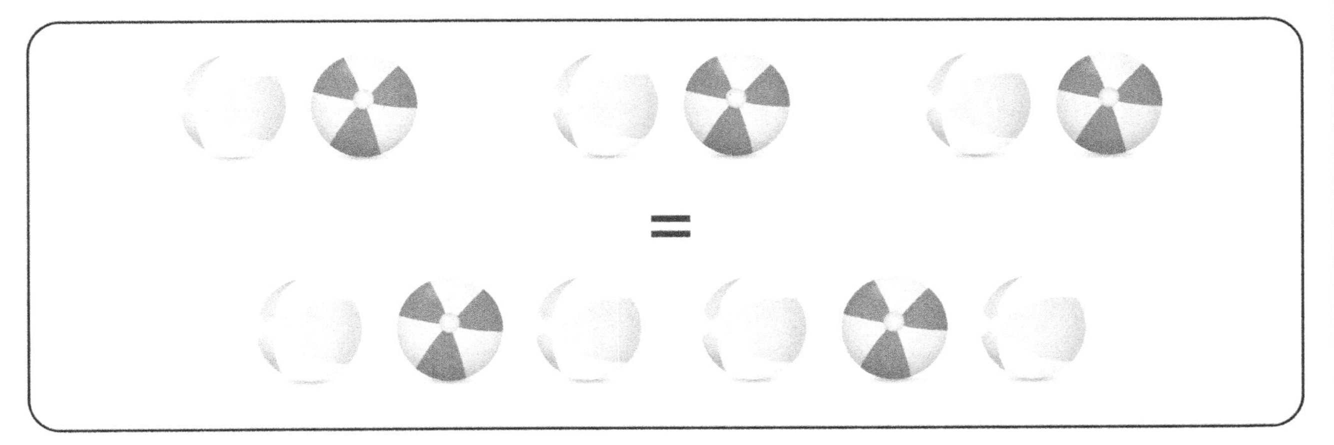

This means that **interchanging** the multiplier and the multiplicand **does not alter** the product or the result of the multiplication.

Also, note that the product is always the largest number in a multiplication sentence.

Special facts about multiplication:

- Any number when multiplied by 1, results in the same number.
- The product of a number and zero is always a zero.

MULTIPLICATION 0 TO 4

Name: ____________________

Date: __________ Time: __________

Score: /50

1. 0 x2	2. 0 x3	3. 0 x3	4. 0 x4	5. 3 x4
6. 2 x1	7. 1 x2	8. 2 x1	9. 4 x3	10. 2 x2
11. 3 x3	12. 3 x0	13. 2 x1	14. 1 x3	15. 3 x4
16. 0 x2	17. 3 x1	18. 3 x3	19. 2 x4	20. 2 x2
21. 3 x4	22. 3 x1	23. 1 x1	24. 2 x2	25. 1 x3
26. 0 x2	27. 0 x1	28. 2 x1	29. 3 x3	30. 2 x2
31. 1 x2	32. 0 x2	33. 1 x3	34. 2 x3	35. 4 x3
36. 1 x2	37. 1 x1	38. 0 x2	39. 3 x1	40. 3 x4
41. 2 x4	42. 1 x2	43. 3 x2	44. 1 x1	45. 3 x3
46. 3 x3	47. 4 x2	48. 3 x4	49. 0 x0	50. 1 x2

MULTIPLICATION 0 TO 4

Name: ____________________

Date: __________ Time: __________

Score: /50

1. 1 x4	2. 2 x1	3. 3 x1	4. 2 x1	5. 4 x1
6. 2 x2	7. 2 x3	8. 1 x3	9. 2 x2	10. 3 x1
11. 1 x2	12. 0 x2	13. 3 x3	14. 4 x0	15. 3 x1
16. 1 x1	17. 4 x1	18. 2 x2	19. 2 x2	20. 4 x1
21. 3 x0	22. 3 x3	23. 1 x1	24. 2 x3	25. 2 x2
26. 4 x2	27. 1 x0	28. 3 x4	29. 2 x0	30. 3 x1
31. 0 x3	32. 0 x0	33. 2 x3	34. 4 x1	35. 1 x4
36. 2 x1	37. 3 x1	38. 0 x4	39. 0 x4	40. 0 x4
41. 4 x2	42. 0 x3	43. 3 x1	44. 1 x3	45. 3 x4
46. 4 x3	47. 4 x1	48. 0 x3	49. 2 x2	50. 0 x2

MULTIPLICATION 0 TO 4

Name: ____________________

Date: ________ Time: ________

Score: /50

1. 2 x2	2. 4 x2	3. 2 x4	4. 1 x1	5. 2 x2
6. 0 x1	7. 2 x0	8. 1 x3	9. 1 x3	10. 4 x2
11. 1 x2	12. 4 x2	13. 1 x3	14. 4 x2	15. 1 x0
16. 1 x1	17. 3 x1	18. 2 x0	19. 2 x1	20. 2 x3
21. 1 x3	22. 2 x2	23. 2 x1	24. 2 x1	25. 2 x2
26. 0 x1	27. 3 x3	28. 1 x4	29. 1 x1	30. 1 x3
31. 3 x2	32. 2 x2	33. 2 x1	34. 2 x2	35. 3 x1
36. 1 x1	37. 2 x4	38. 1 x1	39. 3 x1	40. 3 x3
41. 1 x0	42. 3 x4	43. 0 x0	44. 3 x3	45. 3 x1
46. 1 x0	47. 1 x2	48. 2 x0	49. 4 x0	50. 0 x2

MULTIPLICATION 0 TO 4

Name: ____________________

Date: __________ Time: __________

Score: /50

1. 2 x3	2. 4 x0	3. 1 x3	4. 0 x2	5. 0 x0
6. 2 x3	7. 1 x4	8. 2 x4	9. 3 x3	10. 2 x2
11. 2 x1	12. 1 x4	13. 2 x4	14. 0 x3	15. 1 x1
16. 1 x2	17. 3 x4	18. 0 x2	19. 2 x2	20. 1 x0
21. 3 x3	22. 1 x2	23. 0 x3	24. 4 x3	25. 0 x2
26. 3 x1	27. 3 x3	28. 4 x3	29. 3 x4	30. 2 x0
31. 4 x3	32. 1 x3	33. 3 x4	34. 3 x4	35. 3 x3
36. 0 x1	37. 1 x0	38. 2 x2	39. 0 x3	40. 0 x4
41. 1 x3	42. 1 x1	43. 2 x0	44. 3 x1	45. 3 x3
46. 0 x0	47. 1 x1	48. 1 x2	49. 4 x2	50. 1 x1

MULTIPLICATION 0 TO 4

Name: ____________________

Date: __________ Time: __________

Score: /50

1. 0 x3	2. 2 x2	3. 1 x3	4. 2 x4	5. 2 x3
6. 2 x2	7. 0 x3	8. 3 x0	9. 2 x1	10. 2 x3
11. 1 x2	12. 3 x3	13. 0 x1	14. 4 x2	15. 2 x1
16. 2 x3	17. 2 x2	18. 2 x1	19. 4 x4	20. 3 x1
21. 4 x2	22. 2 x2	23. 1 x1	24. 1 x4	25. 2 x4
26. 2 x2	27. 2 x3	28. 3 x2	29. 2 x4	30. 0 x1
31. 2 x2	32. 2 x0	33. 3 x3	34. 2 x2	35. 3 x2
36. 2 x3	37. 4 x0	38. 0 x2	39. 1 x3	40. 3 x3
41. 3 x3	42. 3 x3	43. 3 x3	44. 1 x0	45. 0 x0
46. 3 x2	47. 3 x1	48. 0 x3	49. 3 x1	50. 1 x1

MULTIPLICATION 0 TO 4

Name: ______________________

Date: __________ Time: __________

Score: /50

1. 4 x4	2. 0 x2	3. 2 x3	4. 3 x1	5. 2 x4
6. 3 x0	7. 1 x2	8. 1 x2	9. 2 x3	10. 1 x2
11. 2 x3	12. 0 x0	13. 1 x4	14. 2 x1	15. 3 x1
16. 0 x2	17. 1 x3	18. 3 x3	19. 4 x3	20. 2 x1
21. 0 x4	22. 1 x3	23. 0 x2	24. 2 x3	25. 1 x2
26. 2 x0	27. 2 x3	28. 2 x2	29. 2 x0	30. 3 x1
31. 3 x1	32. 1 x3	33. 2 x3	34. 4 x2	35. 3 x4
36. 1 x4	37. 3 x1	38. 2 x1	39. 3 x4	40. 3 x4
41. 0 x1	42. 2 x0	43. 2 x3	44. 0 x2	45. 1 x2
46. 2 x2	47. 0 x0	48. 3 x1	49. 3 x3	50. 3 x1

MULTIPLICATION 0 TO 4

Name: ______________________

Date: __________ Time: __________

Score: /50

1. 1 x1	2. 3 x3	3. 4 x2	4. 3 x1	5. 1 x3
6. 2 x4	7. 1 x4	8. 1 x2	9. 3 x1	10. 2 x3
11. 3 x3	12. 3 x0	13. 1 x1	14. 4 x1	15. 4 x1
16. 3 x3	17. 0 x0	18. 1 x1	19. 2 x1	20. 2 x2
21. 3 x2	22. 1 x0	23. 3 x1	24. 2 x1	25. 1 x2
26. 3 x4	27. 3 x0	28. 1 x3	29. 4 x2	30. 1 x3
31. 2 x0	32. 3 x2	33. 1 x0	34. 1 x1	35. 3 x3
36. 1 x2	37. 4 x4	38. 1 x3	39. 3 x2	40. 2 x3
41. 0 x1	42. 1 x4	43. 1 x1	44. 1 x2	45. 3 x0
46. 1 x4	47. 2 x3	48. 0 x0	49. 1 x1	50. 1 x3

MULTIPLICATION 0 TO 4

Name: ______________________

Date: __________ Time: __________

Score: /50

1. 4 x0	2. 2 x4	3. 0 x2	4. 1 x3	5. 4 x1
6. 2 x0	7. 1 x1	8. 2 x3	9. 2 x2	10. 1 x3
11. 4 x2	12. 1 x1	13. 2 x1	14. 2 x2	15. 4 x3
16. 3 x2	17. 2 x2	18. 1 x2	19. 3 x4	20. 3 x2
21. 0 x3	22. 1 x0	23. 2 x1	24. 1 x1	25. 3 x4
26. 4 x1	27. 3 x2	28. 1 x4	29. 1 x0	30. 2 x0
31. 3 x4	32. 4 x1	33. 1 x2	34. 2 x0	35. 4 x2
36. 1 x1	37. 2 x0	38. 4 x1	39. 2 x2	40. 4 x0
41. 3 x0	42. 1 x0	43. 0 x0	44. 2 x3	45. 2 x3
46. 3 x2	47. 2 x3	48. 1 x2	49. 2 x1	50. 0 x3

ACTIVITY CORNER

MULTIPLY THE NUMBERS

4 x 4 =

0 x 2 =

2 x 3 =

5 x 1 =

WORD PROBLEMS
MULTIPLICATION 0 TO 4

Name: ____________________
Date: __________ Time: __________

1. There are 2 bells in a pack. How many bells are there in 3 packs?

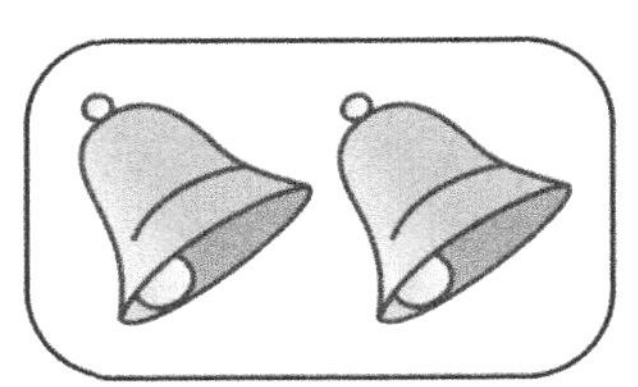

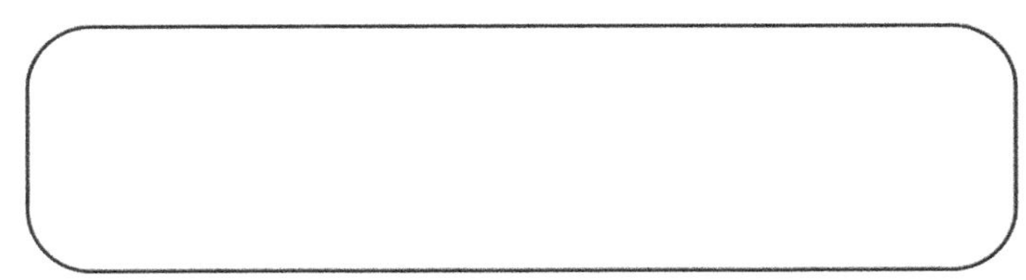

Answer

2. Andrew does not have money to buy crayons. Each of his 4 friends gives him 3 crayons. How many crayons does Andrew have now?

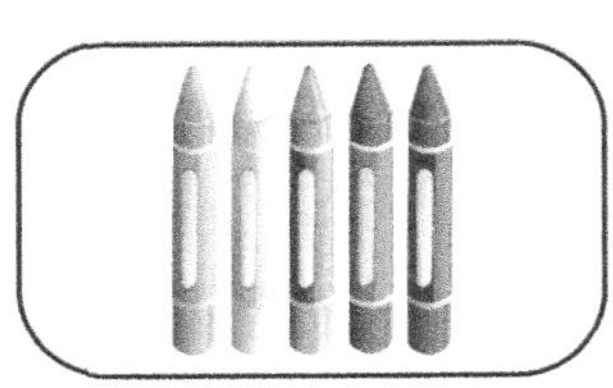

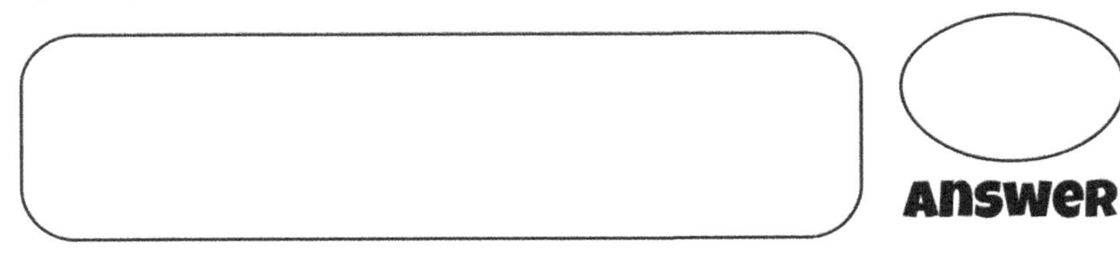

Answer

3. Ivy uses 4 paper clips to measure her pen. Each clip is 2 inches long. How long is the pen?

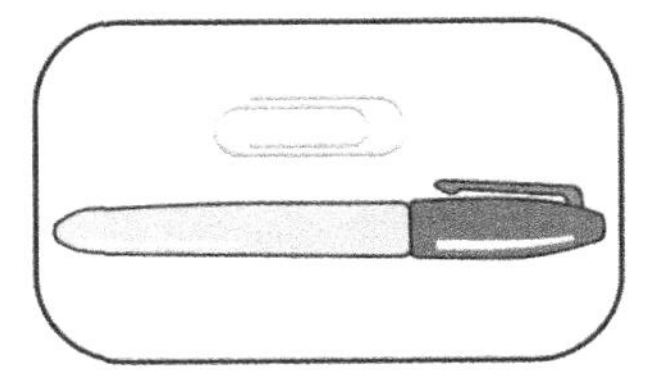

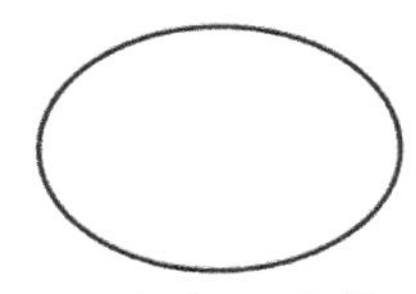

Answer

4. There are 2 boxes with 4 soda cans in each box. How many soda cans are there?

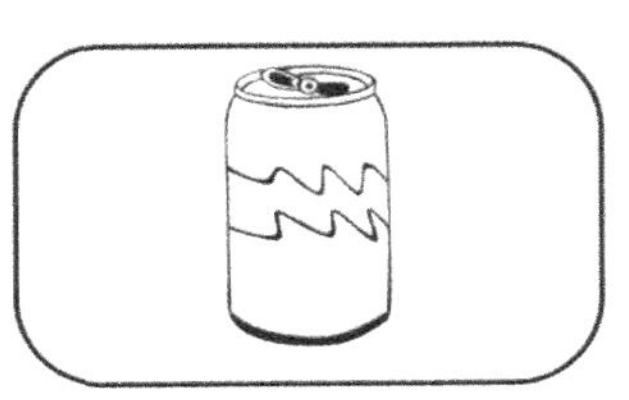

Answer

WORD PROBLEMS
MULTIPLICATION 0 TO 4

Name: ______________________
Date: __________ Time: __________

5. Each pig has 4 legs. How many legs do 4 pigs have?

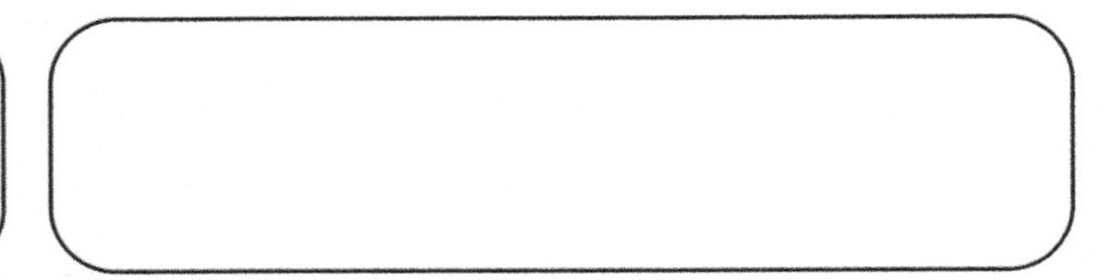

ANSWER

6. Mike runs 2 miles for 4 days in a row. How many miles does he run in 4 days?

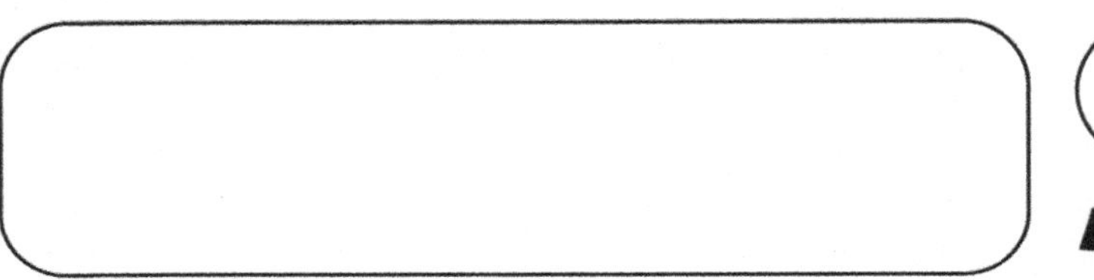
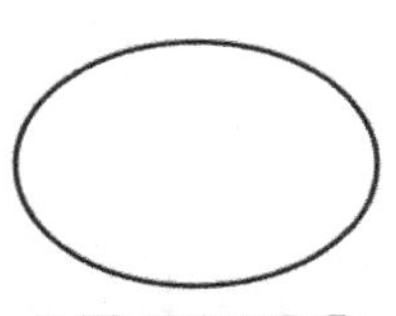

ANSWER

7. Sophia writes 3 paragraphs in each essay. She writes 3 essays. How many paragraphs does she write in all?

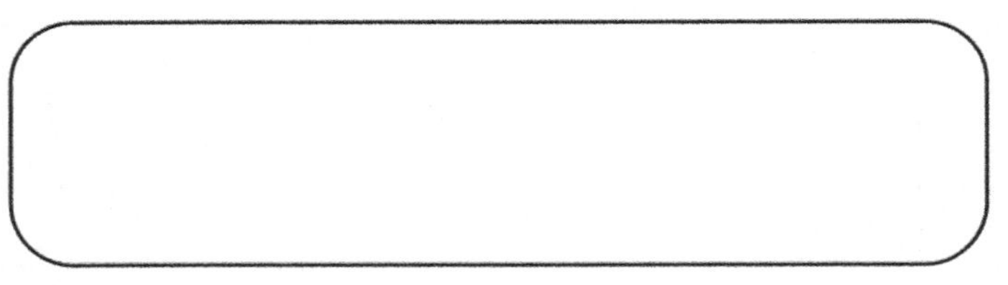
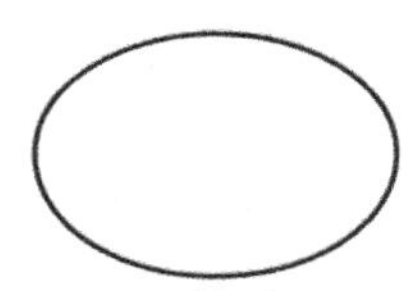

ANSWER

8. There are 4 tables in the cafeteria with 3 children on each table. How many children are there altogether?

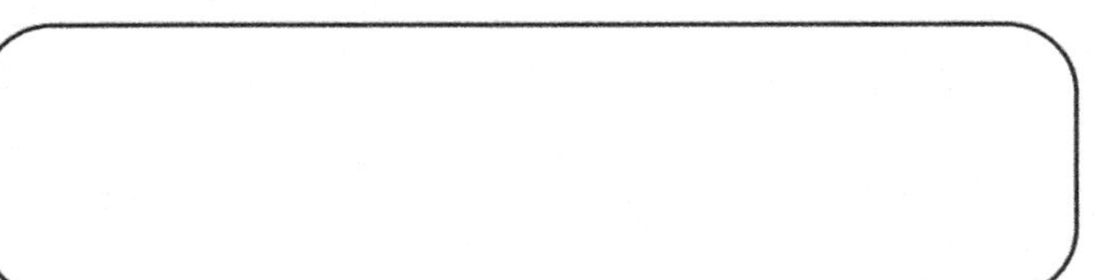

ANSWER

WORD PROBLEMS
MULTIPLICATION 0 TO 4

Name: ____________________

Date: __________ Time: __________

9. Alice uses 3 tiny pencils to measure her pencil case. Each pencil measures 3 inches. What is the length of the pencil case?

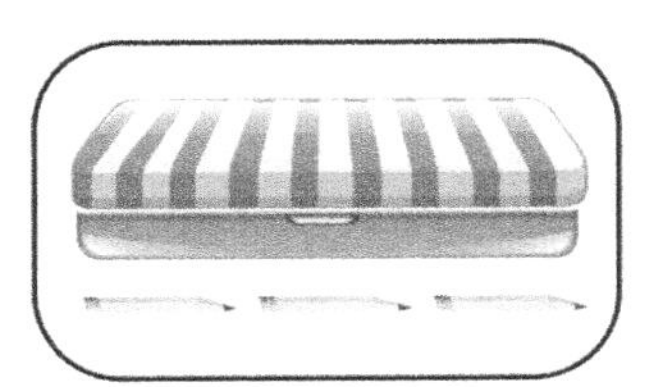

ANSWER

10. Jeffrey uses 4 pencils to measure a rope. Each pencil measures 3 inches. What is the length of the rope?

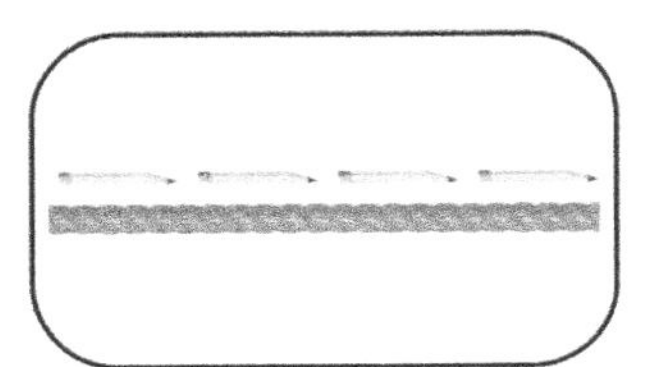

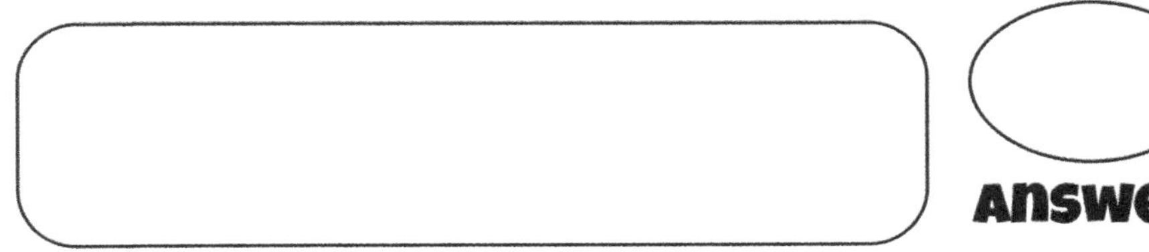

ANSWER

11. Each hen has 2 wings. If there are 3 hens, how many wings are there?

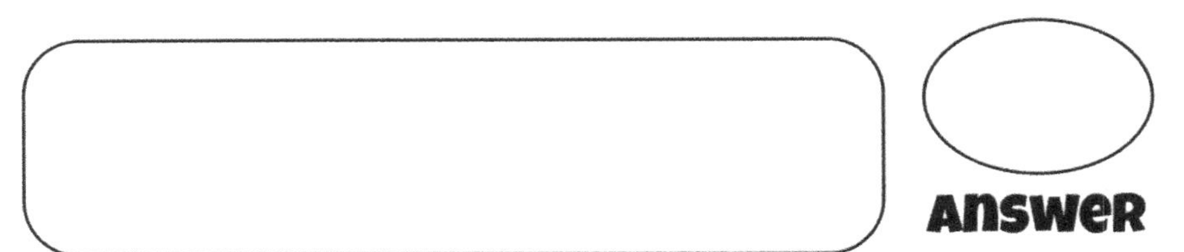

ANSWER

12. There are 4 candies in each pack. How many candies are there in 4 packs?

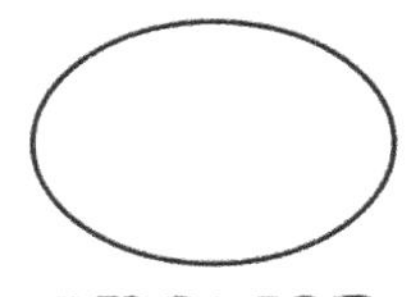

ANSWER

ACTIVITY CORNER

MULTIPLY THE NUMBERS

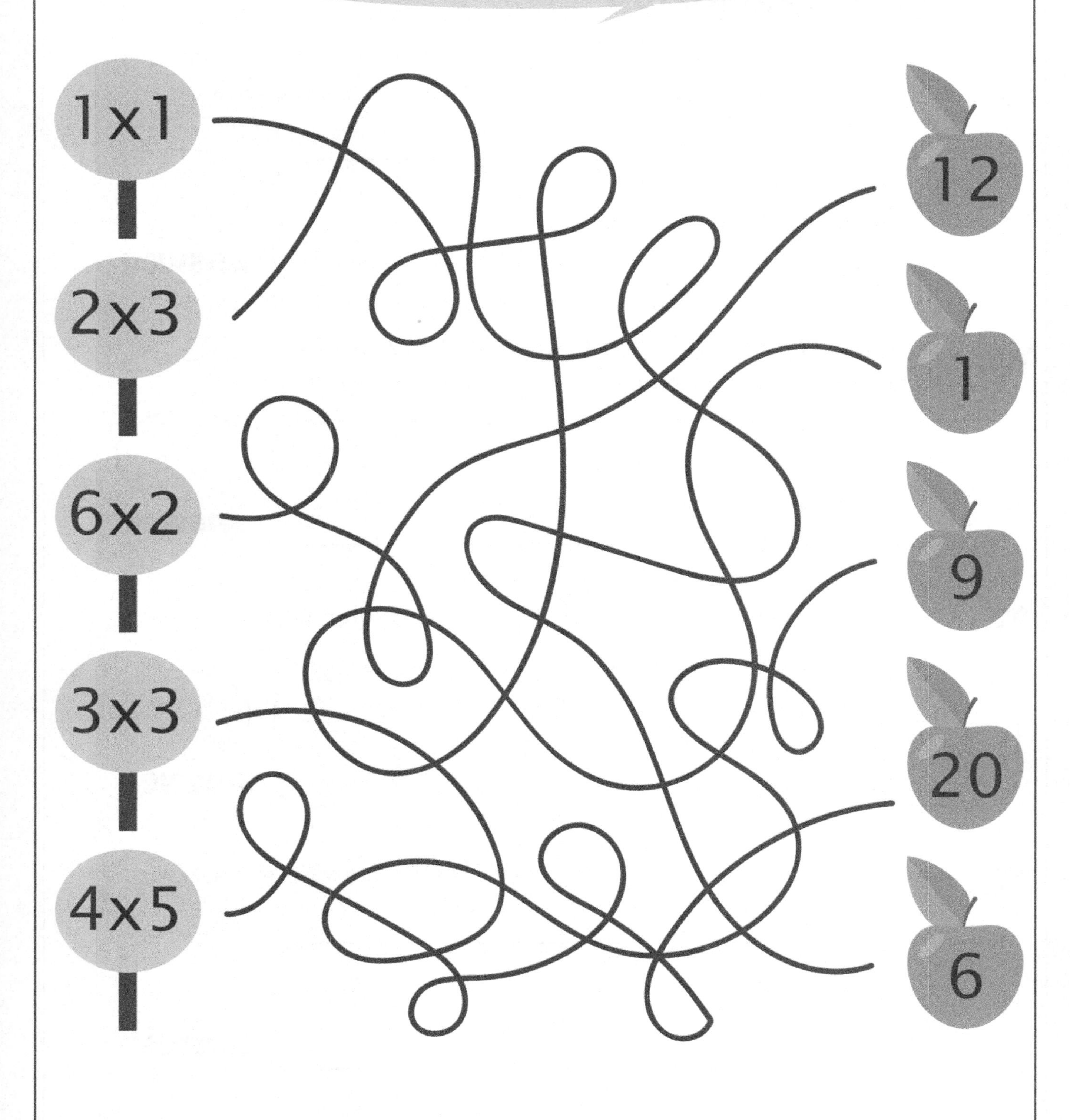

WORD PROBLEMS
MULTIPLICATION 0 TO 4

Name: ____________________

Date: __________ Time: __________

13. A phone takes 2 hours to charge. If there are 3 phones, how many hours will it take to charge them all?

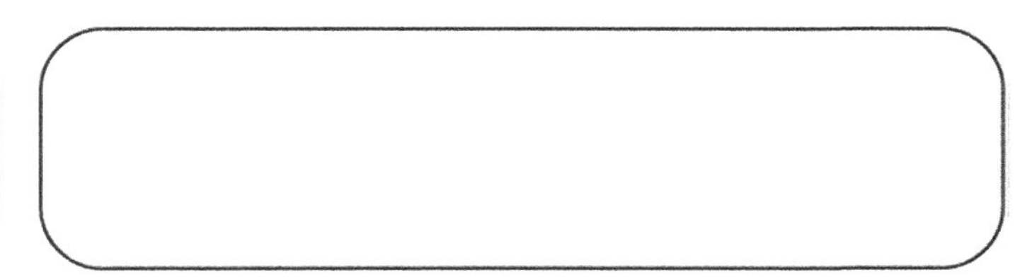

ANSWER

14. There are 4 racks of books. Each rack has 4 books. How many books are there?

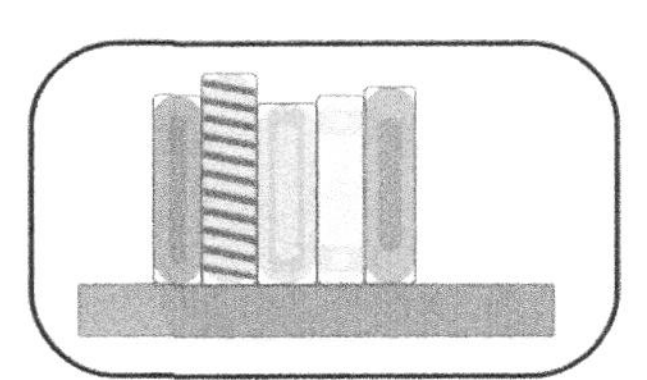
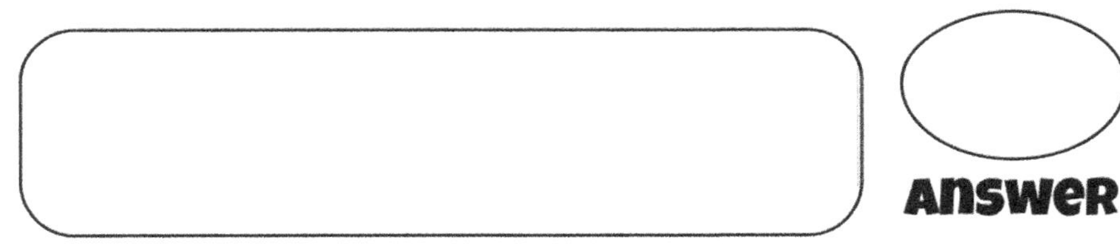

ANSWER

15. Monica has 2 brothers. Each of them gave her $4. How much money does Monica have now?

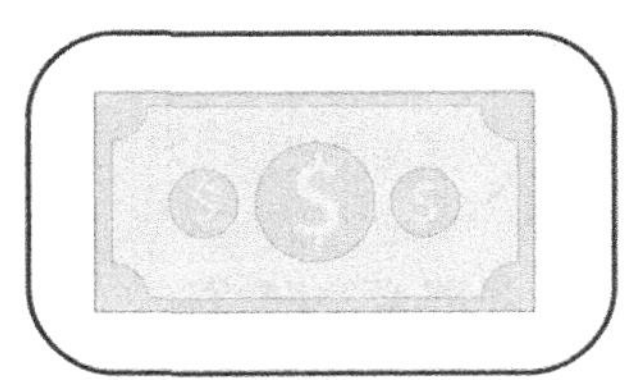
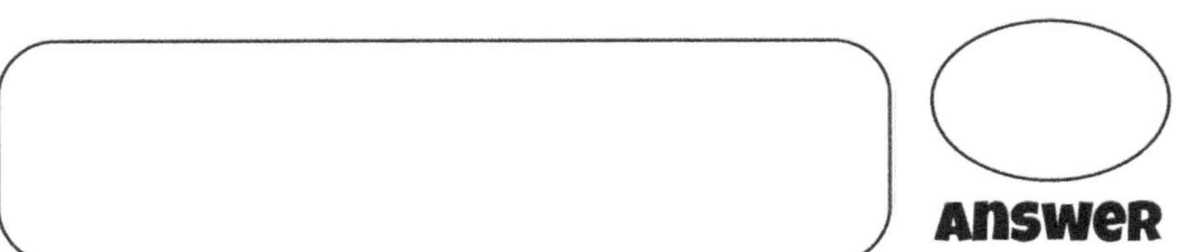

ANSWER

16. There are 3 children. Each of them has 3 marbles. How many marbles do they have altogether?

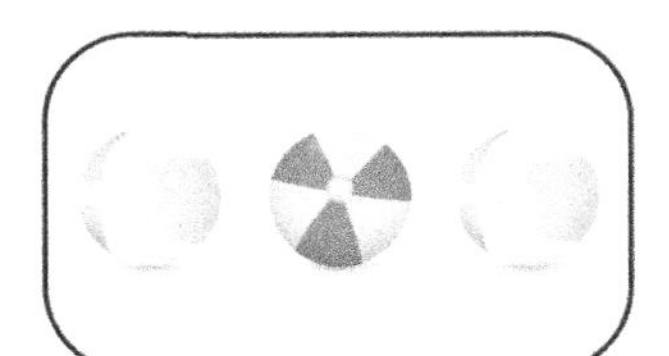
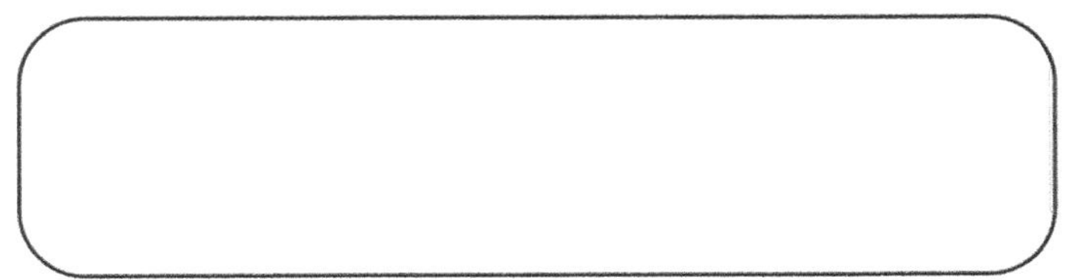

ANSWER

WORD PROBLEMS
MULTIPLICATION 0 TO 4

Name: ____________________

Date: __________ Time: __________

17. Gale packed 2 muffins in each snack box. There are 4 snack boxes. How many muffins are there?

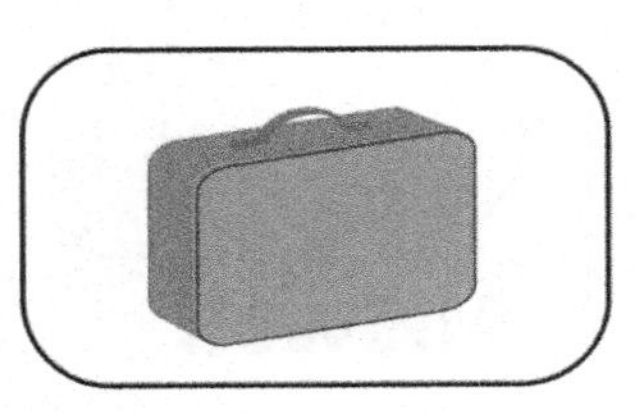

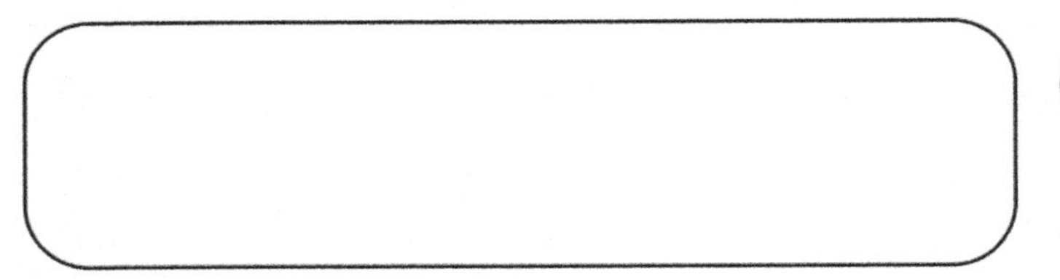

ANSWER

18. Will arrange 3 pineapples in a row. There are 4 rows. How many pineapples are there?

ANSWER

19. There are 3 light bulbs in each room. How many light bulbs are there in 2 rooms?

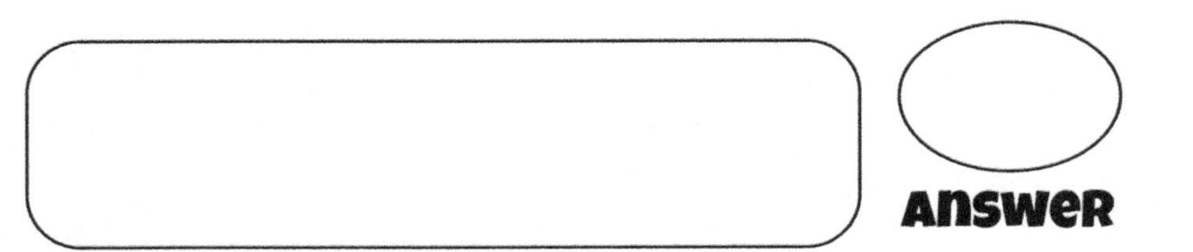

ANSWER

20. There are 4 children in the house, and each child receives 4 notebooks. How many notebooks are there?

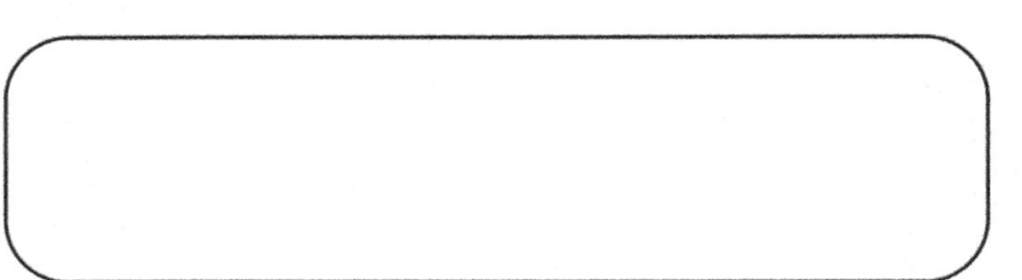

ANSWER

WORD PROBLEMS
MULTIPLICATION 0 TO 4

Name: ______________________

Date: __________ Time: __________

21. Gwen has 2 pencil cases. Haley has twice as many pencil cases as Gwen. How many pencil cases does Haley have?

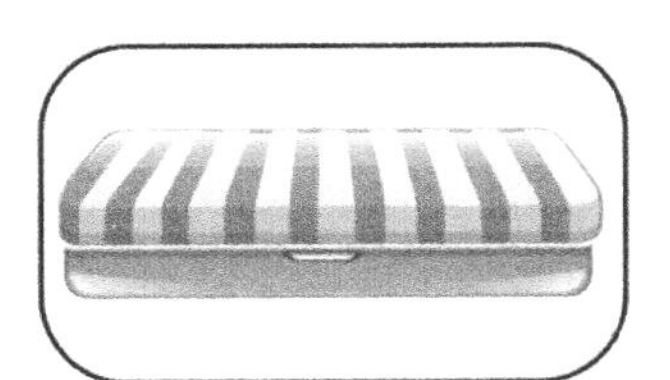

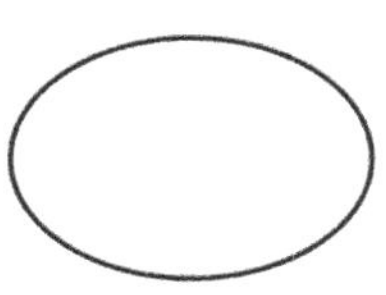

Answer

22. Ben waters 4 plants. Dan waters twice as many plants as Ben. How many plants does Dan water?

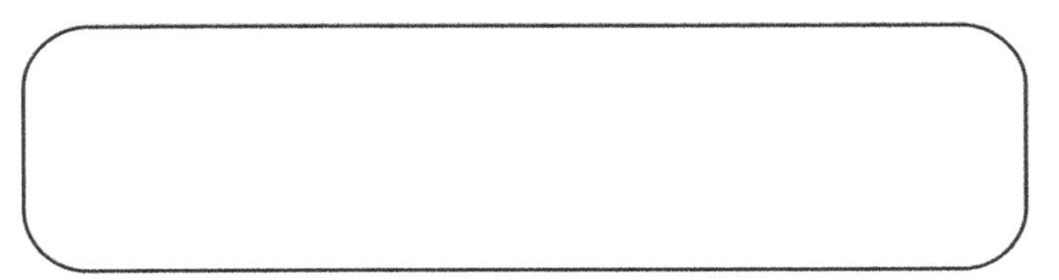
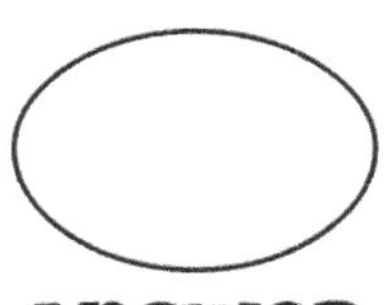

Answer

23. If a snack pack costs $3, how much will 4 snack packs cost?

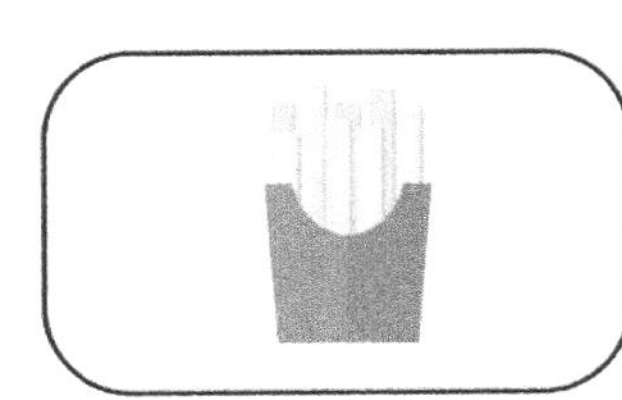

Answer

24. Jose has 3 caps. Erika has two times as that many caps. How many caps does Erika have?

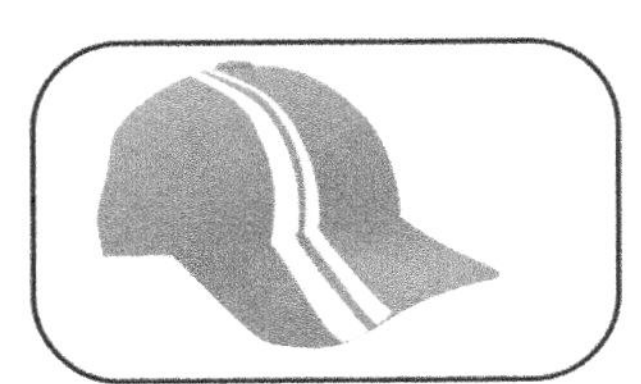

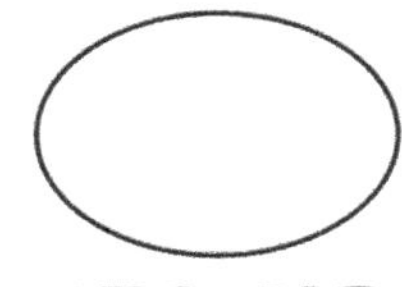

Answer

WORD PROBLEMS
MULTIPLICATION 0 TO 4

Name: ______________________

Date: __________ Time: __________

25. Shane has 3 pillows. Cara has thrice as many pillows as Shane. How many pillows does Cara have?

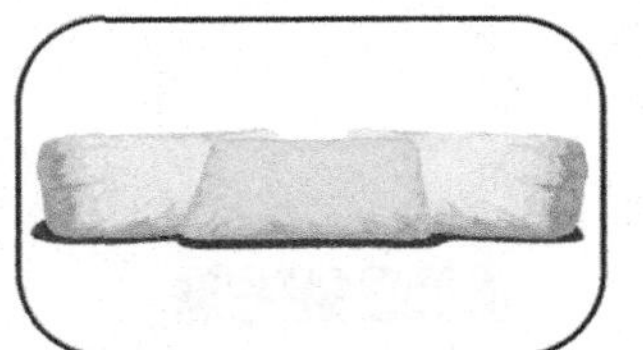

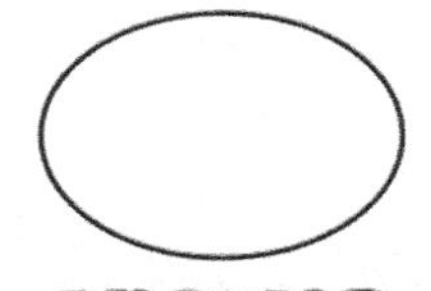

ANSWER

FIND A WAY

MULTIPLICATION 5 TO 8

Name: ____________________

Date: __________ Time: __________

Score: /50

1. 7 x8	2. 7 x6	3. 8 x7	4. 6 x6	5. 8 x7
6. 6 x8	7. 6 x6	8. 7 x5	9. 7 x8	10. 7 x5
11. 6 x6	12. 5 x6	13. 7 x6	14. 7 x8	15. 7 x7
16. 6 x6	17. 6 x5	18. 6 x8	19. 8 x7	20. 5 x6
21. 7 x6	22. 6 x6	23. 6 x5	24. 7 x7	25. 6 x6
26. 7 x7	27. 7 x8	28. 6 x6	29. 7 x7	30. 7 x6
31. 7 x8	32. 6 x7	33. 6 x6	34. 6 x6	35. 6 x5
36. 5 x7	37. 8 x8	38. 7 x7	39. 7 x5	40. 6 x6
41. 7 x8	42. 7 x7	43. 7 x7	44. 7 x6	45. 7 x6
46. 7 x7	47. 5 x6	48. 7 x6	49. 7 x7	50. 5 x8

MULTIPLICATION 5 TO 8

Name: ____________________

Date: __________ Time: __________

Score: /50

1. 7 x7	2. 7 x7	3. 6 x7	4. 7 x8	5. 7 x5
6. 8 x8	7. 7 x6	8. 7 x7	9. 6 x6	10. 5 x7
11. 6 x7	12. 7 x5	13. 5 x8	14. 8 x5	15. 6 x7
16. 7 x8	17. 7 x7	18. 7 x6	19. 6 x6	20. 6 x6
21. 5 x6	22. 5 x6	23. 6 x7	24. 6 x6	25. 6 x7
26. 6 x8	27. 8 x6	28. 7 x6	29. 6 x5	30. 8 x8
31. 5 x8	32. 7 x7	33. 8 x6	34. 7 x5	35. 7 x6
36. 5 x6	37. 7 x6	38. 6 x7	39. 6 x6	40. 7 x6
41. 6 x6	42. 6 x7	43. 6 x7	44. 6 x7	45. 7 x6
46. 6 x7	47. 8 x6	48. 6 x7	49. 6 x6	50. 7 x7

MULTIPLICATION 5 TO 8

Name: ____________________

Date: __________ Time: __________

Score: /50

1. 6 x7	2. 6 x5	3. 5 x7	4. 6 x6	5. 6 x5
6. 6 x6	7. 6 x7	8. 7 x7	9. 6 x6	10. 6 x8
11. 7 x7	12. 6 x6	13. 6 x6	14. 6 x6	15. 6 x6
16. 8 x7	17. 7 x6	18. 7 x8	19. 8 x8	20. 6 x6
21. 7 x7	22. 7 x7	23. 6 x6	24. 6 x6	25. 6 x8
26. 8 x5	27. 6 x7	28. 5 x7	29. 7 x7	30. 8 x5
31. 6 x6	32. 7 x8	33. 6 x8	34. 7 x6	35. 7 x5
36. 7 x5	37. 8 x6	38. 5 x5	39. 7 x8	40. 6 x7
41. 7 x6	42. 6 x7	43. 8 x7	44. 6 x7	45. 8 x6
46. 8 x5	47. 7 x7	48. 7 x5	49. 7 x7	50. 6 x7

MULTIPLICATION 5 TO 8

Name: ____________________

Date: ________ Time: ________

Score: /50

1. 8 x6 ___	2. 8 x7 ___	3. 8 x5 ___	4. 6 x5 ___	5. 5 x6 ___
6. 7 x7 ___	7. 6 x5 ___	8. 5 x6 ___	9. 7 x6 ___	10. 7 x6 ___
11. 6 x8 ___	12. 7 x7 ___	13. 6 x7 ___	14. 7 x8 ___	15. 8 x8 ___
16. 7 x7 ___	17. 7 x6 ___	18. 8 x7 ___	19. 6 x6 ___	20. 7 x5 ___
21. 5 x7 ___	22. 6 x7 ___	23. 8 x5 ___	24. 7 x6 ___	25. 5 x6 ___
26. 8 x6 ___	27. 7 x7 ___	28. 5 x7 ___	29. 6 x6 ___	30. 6 x5 ___
31. 6 x7 ___	32. 6 x6 ___	33. 5 x6 ___	34. 8 x6 ___	35. 8 x6 ___
36. 6 x5 ___	37. 7 x7 ___	38. 6 x7 ___	39. 7 x8 ___	40. 7 x6 ___
41. 5 x7 ___	42. 8 x6 ___	43. 5 x8 ___	44. 6 x6 ___	45. 5 x8 ___
46. 7 x8 ___	47. 7 x7 ___	48. 6 x8 ___	49. 7 x6 ___	50. 6 x7 ___

MULTIPLICATION 5 TO 8

Name: ______________________

Date: __________ Time: __________

Score: /50

1. 7 x6	2. 6 x7	3. 7 x8	4. 8 x6	5. 6 x8
6. 7 x7	7. 6 x6	8. 7 x7	9. 5 x6	10. 5 x7
11. 8 x8	12. 5 x8	13. 7 x6	14. 8 x7	15. 5 x5
16. 6 x6	17. 5 x6	18. 6 x7	19. 5 x5	20. 6 x8
21. 6 x6	22. 7 x6	23. 6 x5	24. 7 x6	25. 7 x6
26. 7 x7	27. 8 x7	28. 7 x6	29. 7 x5	30. 5 x8
31. 8 x7	32. 6 x5	33. 6 x8	34. 6 x8	35. 6 x7
36. 6 x7	37. 8 x6	38. 7 x7	39. 6 x6	40. 6 x6
41. 8 x8	42. 7 x6	43. 5 x6	44. 6 x6	45. 6 x5
46. 7 x7	47. 6 x8	48. 5 x7	49. 5 x6	50. 6 x7

MULTIPLICATION 5 TO 8

Name: ____________________

Date: __________ Time: __________

Score: /50

1. 6 x7	2. 7 x7	3. 7 x6	4. 5 x6	5. 7 x7
6. 6 x6	7. 6 x6	8. 7 x6	9. 7 x6	10. 6 x5
11. 8 x8	12. 6 x7	13. 6 x7	14. 6 x5	15. 8 x7
16. 7 x7	17. 7 x8	18. 6 x6	19. 7 x7	20. 7 x7
21. 5 x6	22. 7 x5	23. 8 x5	24. 7 x5	25. 5 x7
26. 7 x6	27. 6 x7	28. 6 x5	29. 6 x5	30. 6 x8
31. 6 x8	32. 6 x6	33. 6 x5	34. 8 x6	35. 7 x7
36. 5 x5	37. 6 x7	38. 6 x5	39. 8 x8	40. 6 x5
41. 7 x7	42. 8 x5	43. 6 x8	44. 7 x7	45. 6 x6
46. 6 x6	47. 7 x7	48. 8 x6	49. 6 x7	50. 5 x6

MULTIPLICATION 5 TO 8

Name: ______________________

Date: __________ Time: __________

Score: /50

1. 5 x6	2. 7 x6	3. 5 x6	4. 7 x7	5. 5 x7
6. 5 x7	7. 7 x6	8. 5 x8	9. 7 x7	10. 5 x6
11. 7 x7	12. 8 x5	13. 5 x6	14. 6 x6	15. 7 x7
16. 7 x7	17. 7 x8	18. 5 x7	19. 7 x5	20. 5 x6
21. 8 x5	22. 6 x6	23. 5 x6	24. 5 x5	25. 7 x6
26. 6 x5	27. 5 x5	28. 5 x8	29. 7 x7	30. 6 x6
31. 5 x7	32. 7 x7	33. 5 x8	34. 7 x7	35. 7 x6
36. 7 x7	37. 5 x6	38. 5 x7	39. 6 x8	40. 8 x6
41. 8 x5	42. 8 x7	43. 8 x7	44. 8 x8	45. 7 x7
46. 7 x7	47. 5 x8	48. 7 x6	49. 7 x8	50. 6 x6

MULTIPLICATION 5 TO 8

Name: ______________________

Date: __________ Time: __________

Score: /50

1. 7 x7 ____	2. 8 x6 ____	3. 5 x7 ____	4. 6 x7 ____	5. 7 x7 ____
6. 6 x7 ____	7. 6 x8 ____	8. 5 x5 ____	9. 5 x6 ____	10. 6 x8 ____
11. 5 x7 ____	12. 8 x6 ____	13. 6 x8 ____	14. 5 x6 ____	15. 7 x8 ____
16. 8 x8 ____	17. 5 x7 ____	18. 5 x7 ____	19. 6 x8 ____	20. 7 x6 ____
21. 7 x7 ____	22. 7 x7 ____	23. 6 x5 ____	24. 8 x8 ____	25. 8 x5 ____
26. 7 x8 ____	27. 5 x8 ____	28. 5 x8 ____	29. 7 x6 ____	30. 6 x6 ____
31. 6 x7 ____	32. 8 x5 ____	33. 5 x7 ____	34. 7 x6 ____	35. 5 x6 ____
36. 5 x7 ____	37. 6 x6 ____	38. 5 x7 ____	39. 8 x7 ____	40. 7 x7 ____
41. 7 x5 ____	42. 6 x6 ____	43. 7 x6 ____	44. 7 x7 ____	45. 6 x8 ____
46. 6 x6 ____	47. 7 x8 ____	48. 7 x5 ____	49. 7 x7 ____	50. 8 x7 ____

FIND THE 10 DIFFERENCES

WORD PROBLEMS
MULTIPLICATION 5 TO 8

Name: ______________________

Date: __________ Time: __________

1. David places 2 candy bars in each bag. If there are 7 bags, how many candy bars are there altogether?

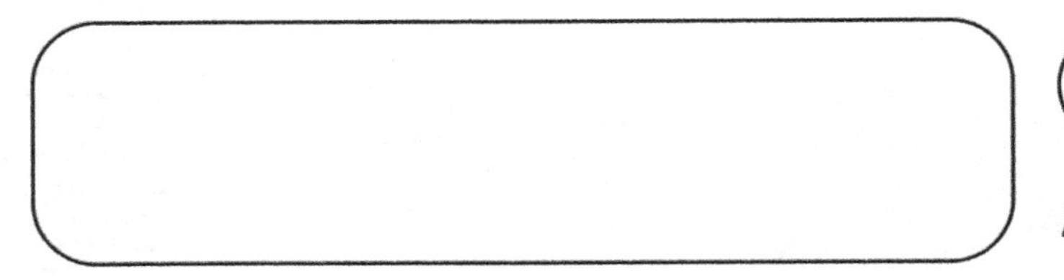

ANSWER

2. There are 6 racks in the gym with 2 footballs on each rack. How many footballs are there altogether?

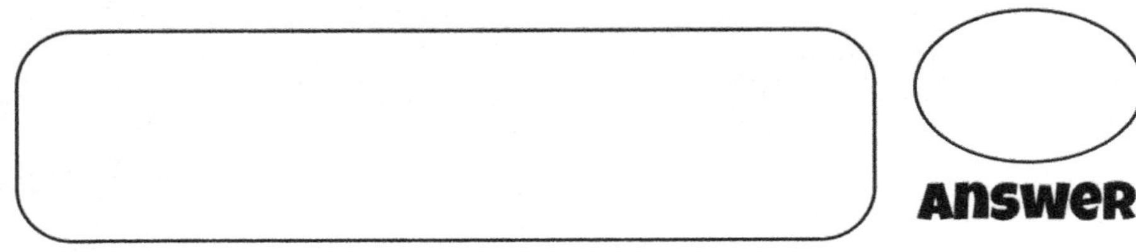

ANSWER

3. There are 5 baskets with 2 carrots in each basket. How many carrots are there altogether?

ANSWER

4. Annie uses a 2-inch eraser to measure the length of her textbook. The textbook is 5 erasers long. What is the length of the textbook in inches?

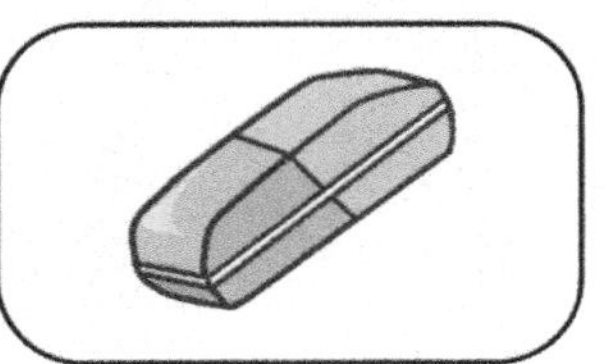

WORD PROBLEMS
MULTIPLICATION 5 TO 8

Name: ____________________

Date: __________ Time: __________

5. An ant has 6 legs. How many legs do 7 ants have?

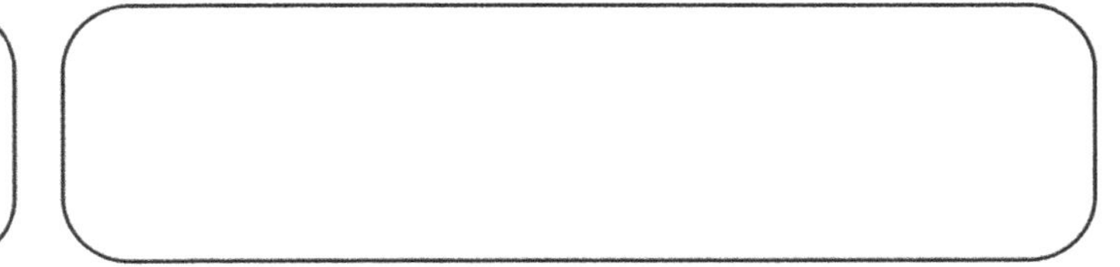
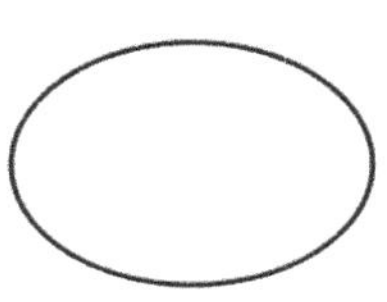

ANSWER

6. Lisa paints 3 meters of the fence each day for a week. How many meters does she paint in a week?

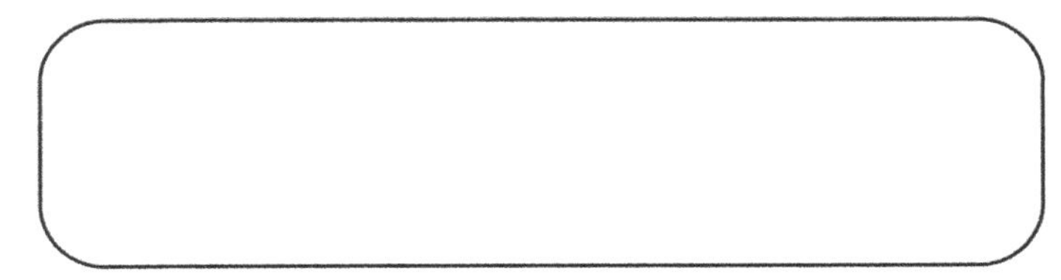
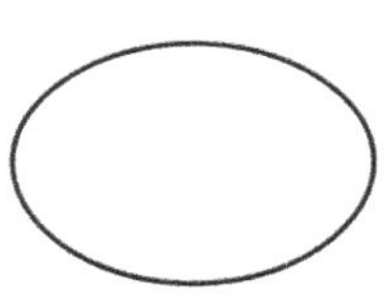

ANSWER

7. Winona rolled a 5, three times in a row. How much did she roll altogether?

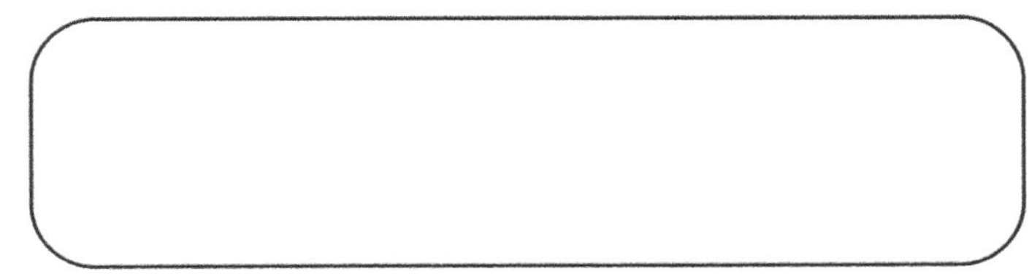
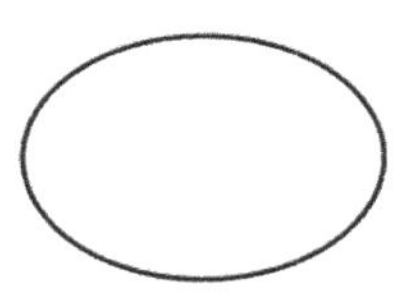

ANSWER

8. Sam takes the dog for a walk twice a day for a week. How many times does she take the dog for walking?

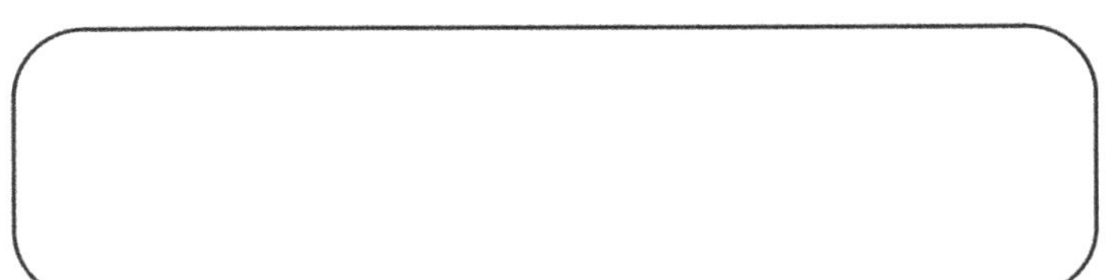
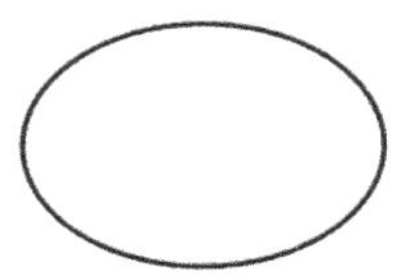

ANSWER

WORD PROBLEMS
MULTIPLICATION 5 TO 8

Name: ____________________

Date: __________ Time: __________

9. There are 7 classrooms in the school with 4 computers in each classroom. How many computers are there all together?

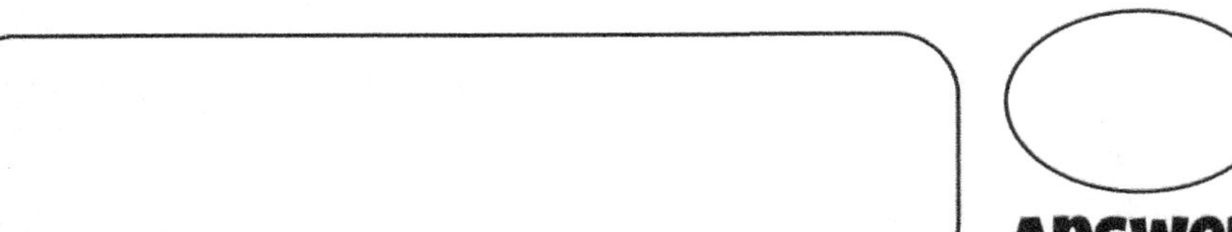

Answer

10. Jack writes 5 paragraphs in each notebook. If there are 8 notebooks, how many paragraphs are there all together?

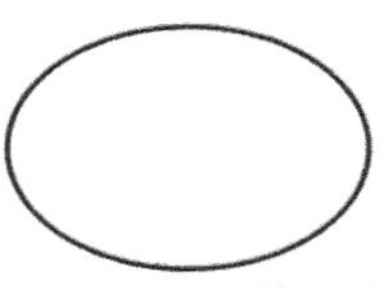

Answer

11. Sue paints 2 portraits for each gallery. If there are 8 galleries, how many portraits are there all together?

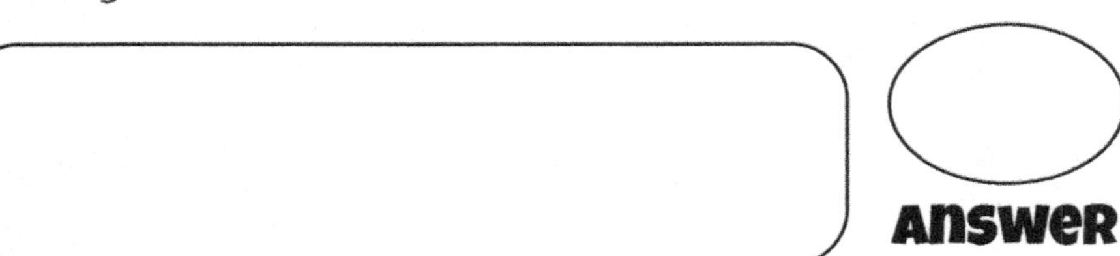

Answer

12. There are 6 short stories in each story book. If there are 8 story books, how many short stories are there altogether

Answer

COLORING ACTIVITY

WORD PROBLEMS
MULTIPLICATION 5 TO 8

Name: ______________________

Date: __________ Time: __________

13. John is 5 years old. His cousin is twice his age. How old is his cousin?

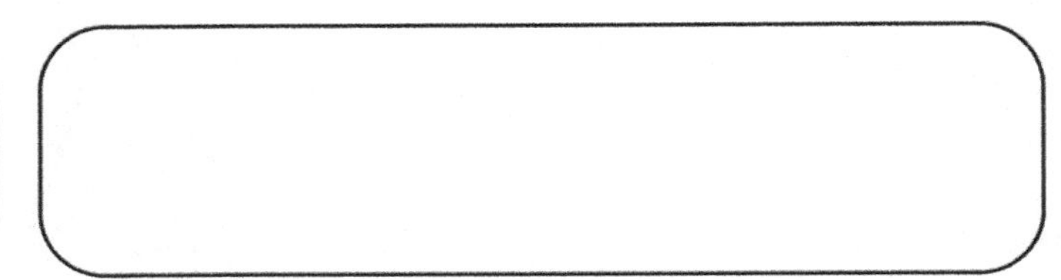

ANSWER

14. Jackie has 2 ribbons of the same length. Each ribbon measures 7 yards. How long will the ribbon be if they are laid in a straight line?

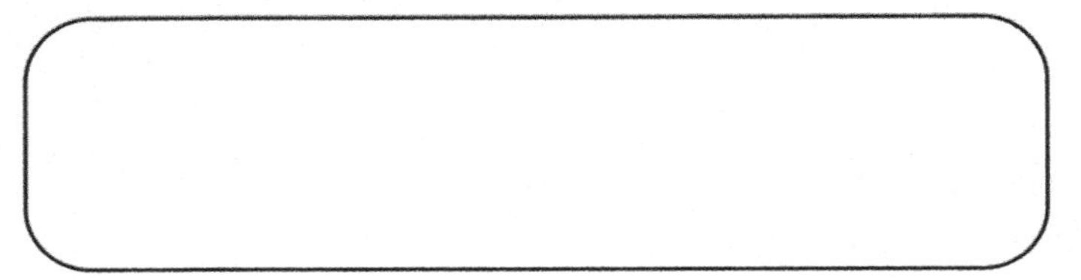

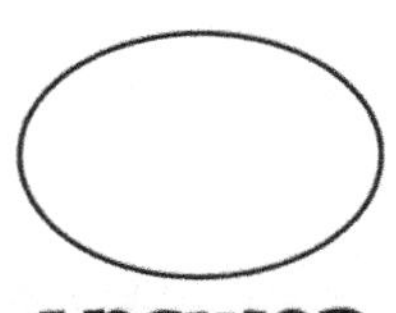

ANSWER

15. There are 7 piles of laundry with 4 towels in each pile. How many towels are there altogether?

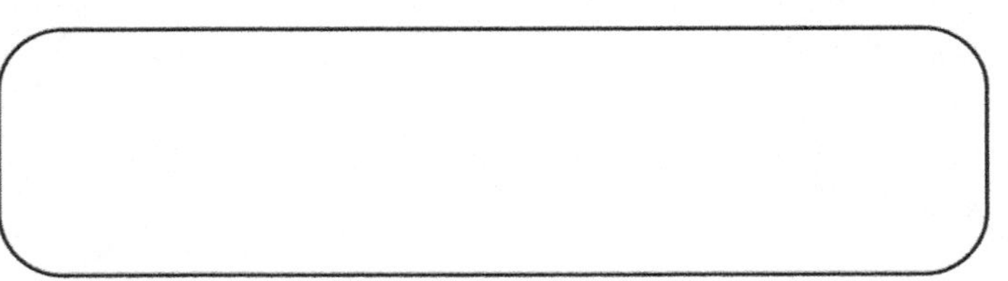

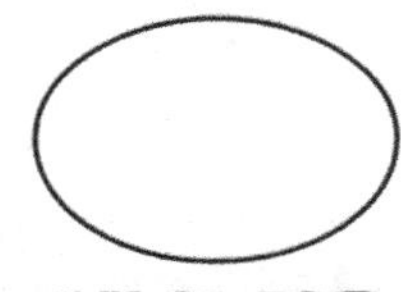

ANSWER

16. Rose puts 8 empty soda cans in each garbage bag. If there are 6 garbage bags, how many empty soda cans are there altogether?

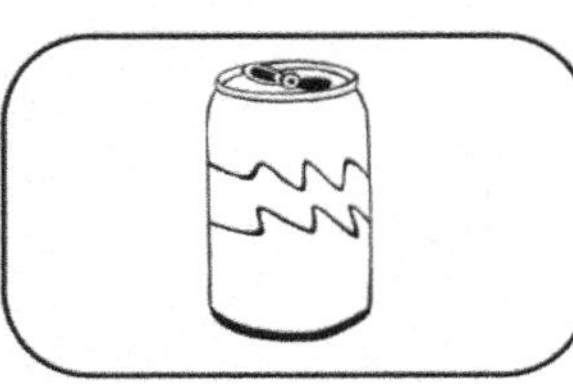

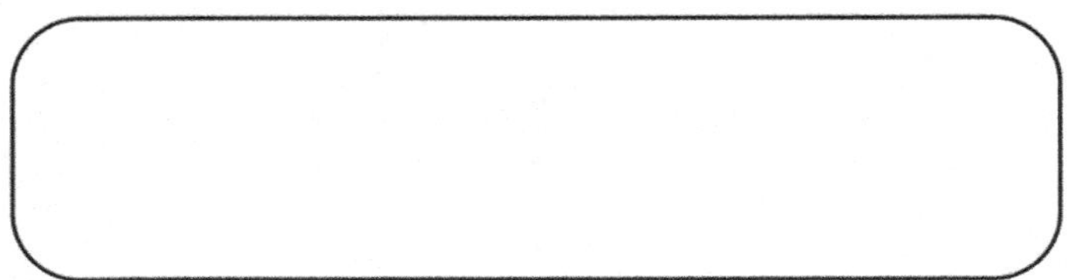

ANSWER

WORD PROBLEMS
MULTIPLICATION 5 TO 8

Name: ______________________
Date: __________ Time: __________

17. There are 6 boxes of eggs. Each box has 6 eggs. How many eggs are there altogether?

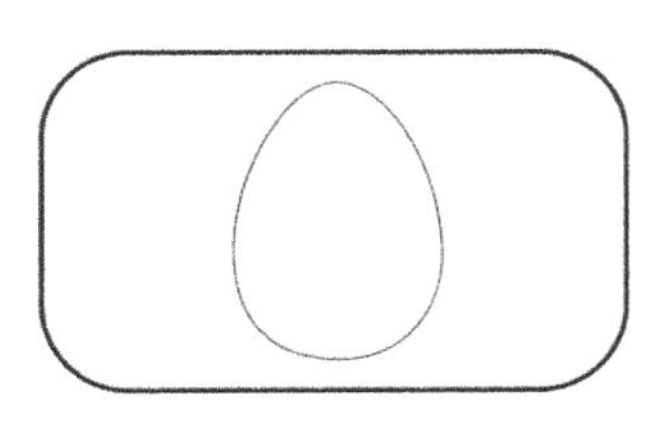
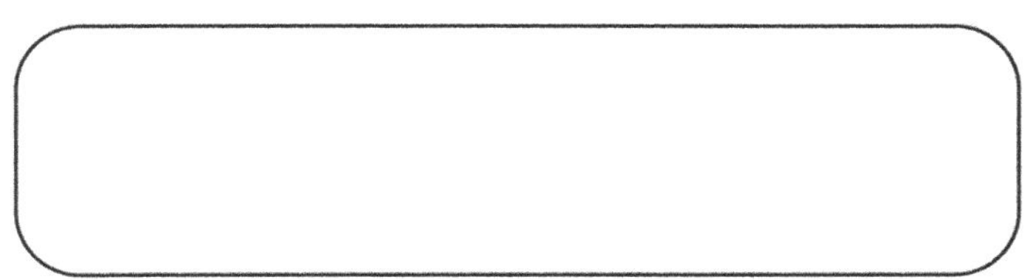

ANSWER

18. My brother and I are playing a board game. We both are on square 1. If I roll 3 sixes in a row, where will I land?

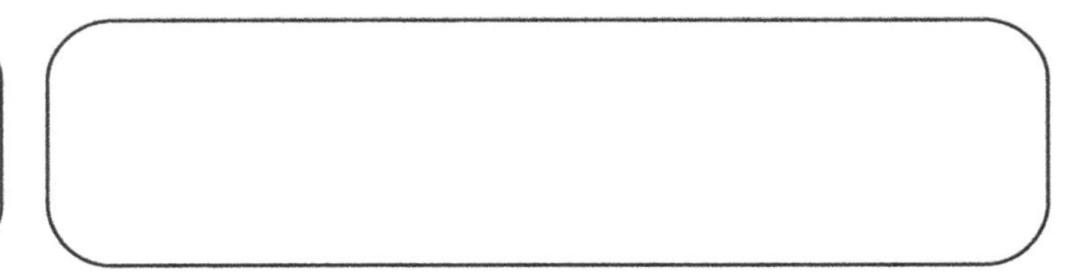
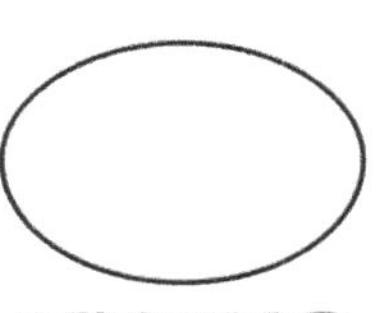

ANSWER

19. There are 8 vases. Each vase holds 8 flowers. How many flowers are there altogether?

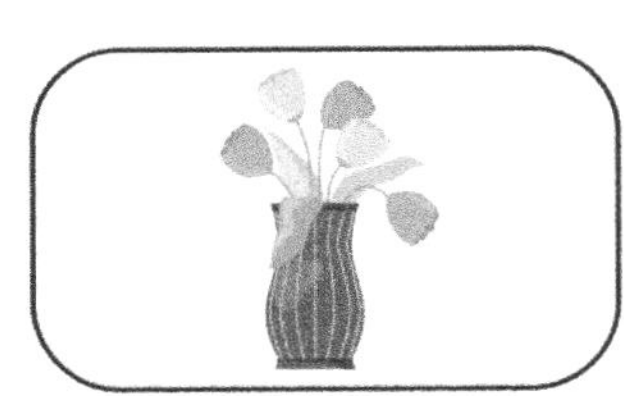

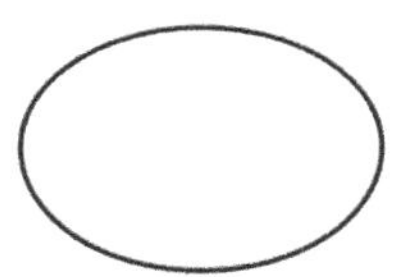

ANSWER

20. Angel draws 5 cylinders. Cody draws twice as many cylinders as Angel. How many cylinders does Cody draw?

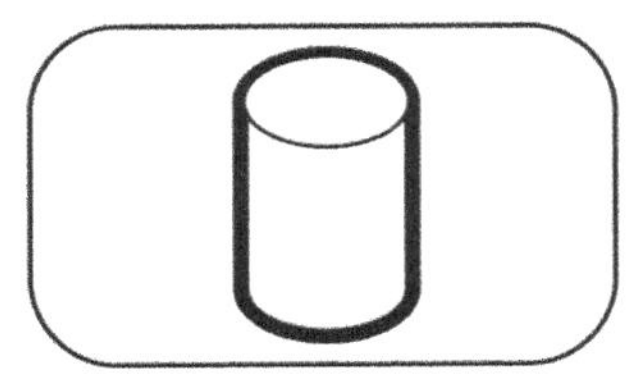

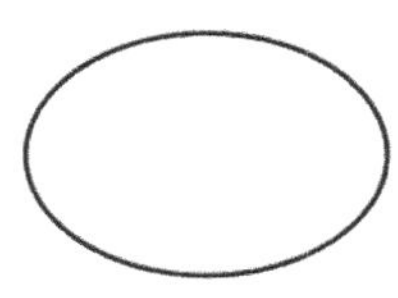

ANSWER

WORD PROBLEMS
MULTIPLICATION 5 TO 8

Name: ____________________

Date: __________ Time: __________

21. A classroom has 5 desks in each row. How many desks are there in 7 rows?

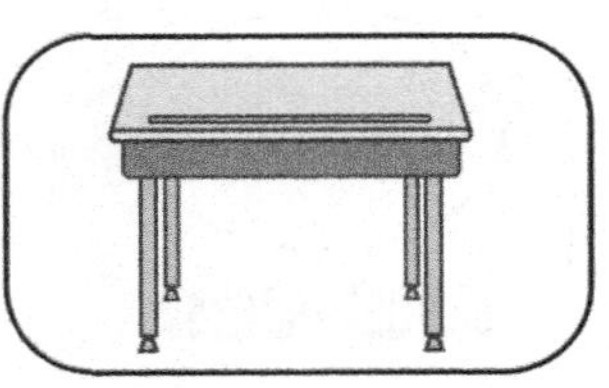

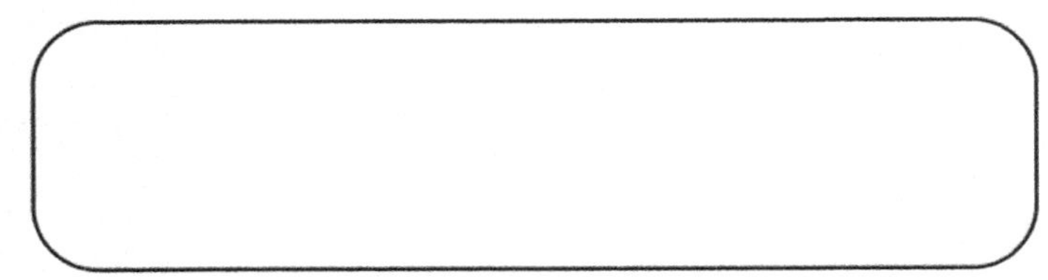

ANSWER

22. There are 5 fingers in each hand. How many fingers are there in 8 hands?

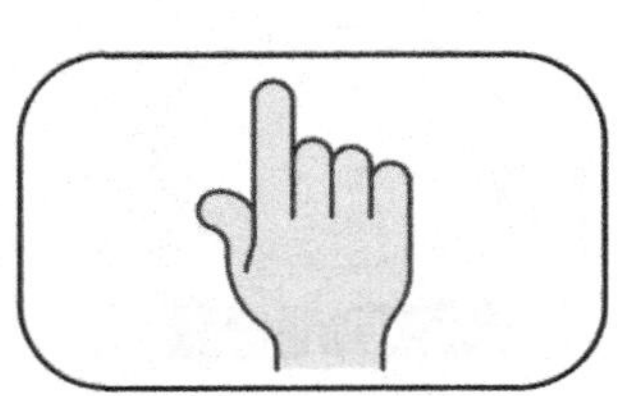

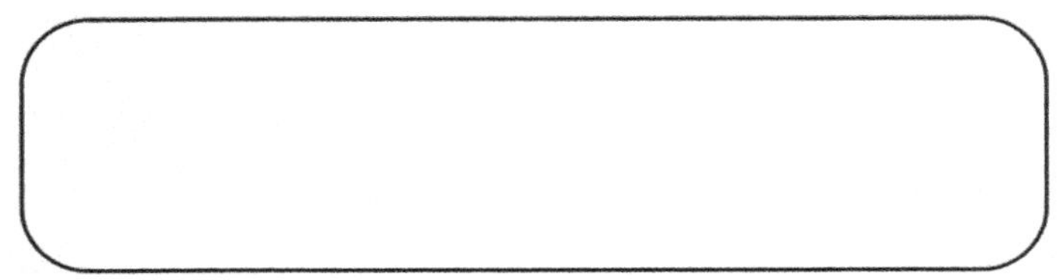

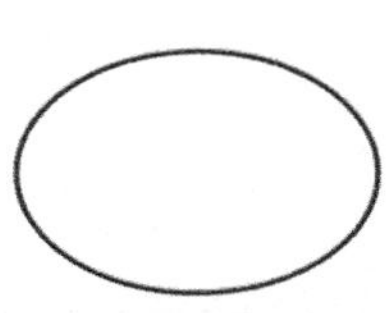

ANSWER

23. A spider has 8 legs. How many legs do 4 spiders have?

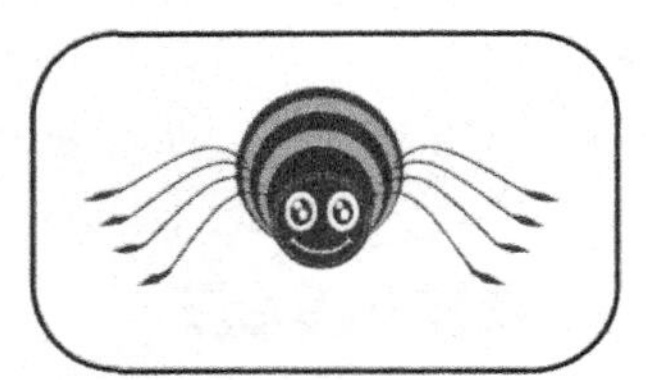

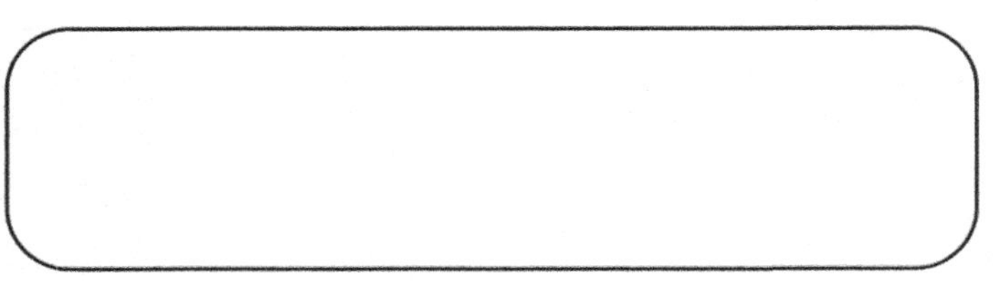

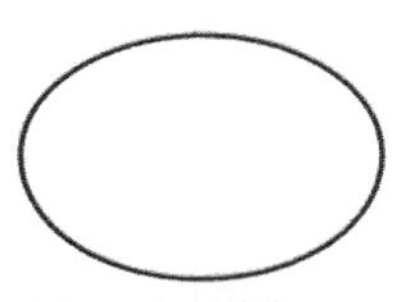

ANSWER

24. There are 7 boxes of cookies. Each box has 8 cookies. How many cookies are there altogether?

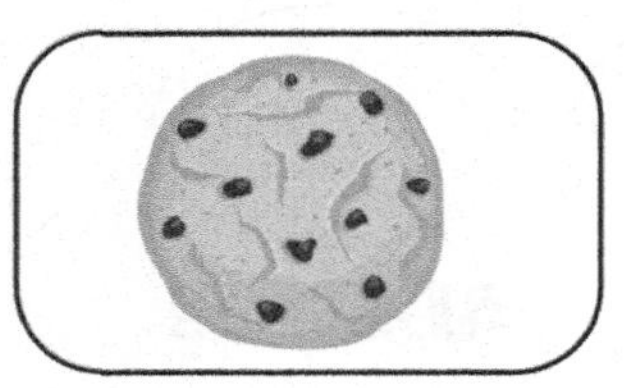

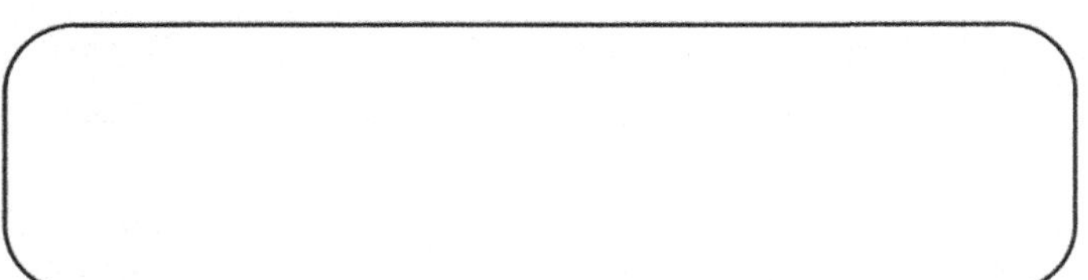

ANSWER

WORD PROBLEMS
MULTIPLICATION 5 TO 8

Name: ____________________

Date: __________ Time: __________

25. There are 3 birds in each cage. There are 8 cages. How many birds are there?

ANSWER

ACTIVITY CORNER

CONNECT THE DOTS

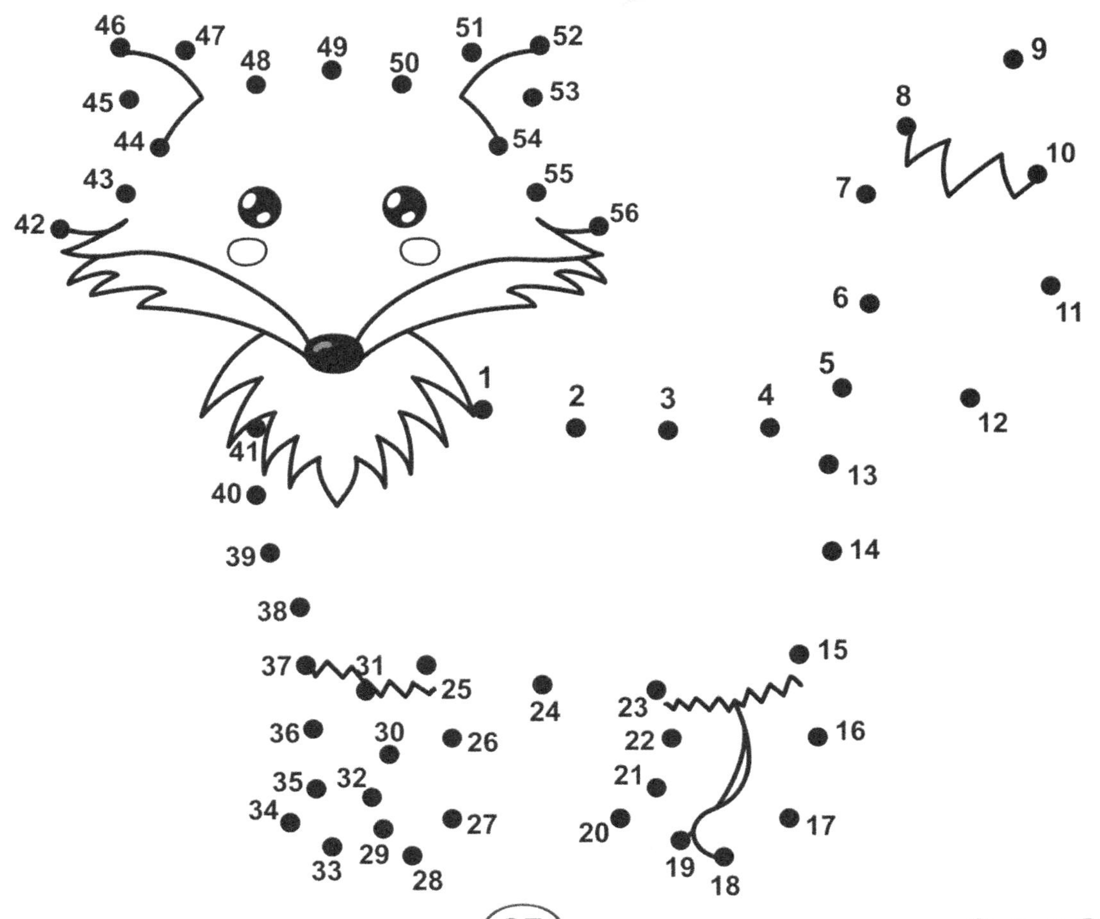

MULTIPLICATION 6 TO 12

Name: ______________________

Date: __________ Time: __________

Score: /50

1. 8 x11	2. 7 x8	3. 7 x10	4. 9 x11	5. 6 x9
6. 11 x11	7. 10 x9	8. 10 x9	9. 9 x11	10. 8 x11
11. 8 x7	12. 8 x7	13. 9 x11	14. 10 x8	15. 11 x9
16. 10 x12	17. 8 x8	18. 12 x12	19. 8 x10	20. 12 x9
21. 9 x6	22. 11 x11	23. 9 x10	24. 10 x9	25. 8 x9
26. 12 x10	27. 11 x8	28. 7 x12	29. 12 x8	30. 12 x12
31. 9 x11	32. 11 x9	33. 8 x7	34. 8 x11	35. 10 x6
36. 10 x7	37. 9 x10	38. 11 x8	39. 7 x11	40. 11 x10
41. 10 x11	42. 10 x10	43. 12 x12	44. 12 x11	45. 10 x6
46. 8 x10	47. 10 x7	48. 7 x10	49. 9 x9	50. 6 x10

MULTIPLICATION 6 TO 12

Name: ____________________
Date: ________ Time: ________

Score: /50

1. 8 x8	2. 7 x9	3. 8 x9	4. 8 x7	5. 7 x10
6. 8 x11	7. 9 x11	8. 9 x9	9. 10 x9	10. 11 x9
11. 7 x10	12. 7 x7	13. 8 x10	14. 11 x6	15. 7 x11
16. 6 x12	17. 11 x8	18. 10 x12	19. 11 x11	20. 9 x11
21. 9 x8	22. 10 x10	23. 10 x7	24. 11 x8	25. 9 x11
26. 9 x7	27. 7 x12	28. 9 x7	29. 8 x9	30. 11 x8
31. 6 x9	32. 9 x10	33. 9 x7	34. 11 x11	35. 12 x7
36. 9 x11	37. 9 x9	38. 7 x10	39. 7 x12	40. 10 x9
41. 7 x6	42. 6 x8	43. 11 x11	44. 8 x6	45. 9 x8
46. 6 x7	47. 9 x8	48. 9 x7	49. 8 x6	50. 12 x12

MULTIPLICATION 6 TO 12

Name: ____________________

Date: __________ Time: __________

Score: /50

1. 9 x8	2. 11 x11	3. 8 x8	4. 7 x7	5. 9 x7
6. 8 x7	7. 6 x12	8. 8 x10	9. 12 x7	10. 10 x10
11. 11 x12	12. 7 x11	13. 6 x7	14. 6 x11	15. 11 x7
16. 8 x12	17. 10 x7	18. 7 x10	19. 8 x8	20. 8 x11
21. 7 x9	22. 11 x11	23. 12 x8	24. 9 x9	25. 12 x7
26. 6 x10	27. 7 x10	28. 10 x10	29. 10 x9	30. 12 x11
31. 12 x9	32. 8 x11	33. 8 x9	34. 11 x10	35. 12 x11
36. 7 x6	37. 9 x11	38. 10 x9	39. 6 x11	40. 9 x9
41. 9 x8	42. 10 x7	43. 11 x7	44. 7 x10	45. 8 x12
46. 9 x11	47. 11 x7	48. 12 x10	49. 10 x8	50. 10 x8

MULTIPLICATION 6 TO 12

Name: ____________________

Date: __________ Time: __________

Score: /50

1. 12 x9	2. 10 x8	3. 12 x6	4. 8 x10	5. 8 x10
6. 8 x11	7. 9 x7	8. 9 x8	9. 9 x12	10. 7 x11
11. 6 x10	12. 8 x11	13. 10 x9	14. 11 x10	15. 8 x6
16. 8 x8	17. 7 x12	18. 8 x7	19. 7 x11	20. 9 x11
21. 7 x6	22. 9 x7	23. 10 x7	24. 8 x8	25. 11 x11
26. 9 x8	27. 11 x6	28. 11 x10	29. 10 x9	30. 6 x7
31. 8 x11	32. 11 x10	33. 11 x9	34. 7 x9	35. 10 x7
36. 9 x8	37. 10 x9	38. 10 x12	39. 11 x11	40. 9 x12
41. 10 x11	42. 7 x9	43. 7 x9	44. 6 x7	45. 10 x8
46. 10 x7	47. 11 x6	48. 11 x10	49. 6 x10	50. 12 x8

MULTIPLICATION 6 TO 12

Name: ______________________

Date: __________ Time: __________

Score: /50

1. 11 x9	2. 12 x8	3. 9 x11	4. 12 x10	5. 9 x10
6. 10 x8	7. 9 x8	8. 10 x10	9. 7 x7	10. 11 x8
11. 12 x8	12. 11 x10	13. 10 x12	14. 11 x7	15. 10 x6
16. 9 x8	17. 9 x11	18. 9 x7	19. 11 x7	20. 8 x10
21. 11 x11	22. 8 x9	23. 6 x9	24. 8 x12	25. 11 x10
26. 9 x9	27. 11 x10	28. 11 x7	29. 9 x9	30. 11 x10
31. 7 x6	32. 7 x12	33. 8 x10	34. 11 x11	35. 6 x9
36. 11 x10	37. 9 x11	38. 11 x10	39. 10 x8	40. 11 x10
41. 6 x11	42. 10 x7	43. 9 x9	44. 11 x10	45. 11 x11
46. 9 x7	47. 10 x7	48. 7 x7	49. 12 x10	50. 11 x6

MULTIPLICATION 6 TO 12

Name: ____________________

Date: ________ Time: ________

Score: /50

1. 12 x8	2. 11 x10	3. 9 x7	4. 9 x9	5. 7 x10
6. 9 x8	7. 11 x11	8. 10 x10	9. 10 x11	10. 6 x8
11. 7 x9	12. 9 x6	13. 9 x9	14. 7 x9	15. 9 x10
16. 10 x11	17. 7 x6	18. 9 x8	19. 8 x12	20. 9 x11
21. 7 x8	22. 9 x11	23. 11 x12	24. 11 x10	25. 11 x6
26. 8 x11	27. 10 x10	28. 7 x7	29. 8 x7	30. 8 x10
31. 9 x12	32. 11 x10	33. 7 x7	34. 10 x11	35. 9 x11
36. 8 x7	37. 7 x10	38. 12 x12	39. 7 x12	40. 12 x6
41. 7 x7	42. 9 x8	43. 12 x8	44. 8 x12	45. 7 x8
46. 11 x8	47. 11 x7	48. 11 x10	49. 8 x10	50. 6 x7

MULTIPLICATION 6 TO 12

Name: ____________________

Date: __________ Time: __________

Score: /50

1. 11 x7
2. 7 x6
3. 8 x9
4. 8 x7
5. 7 x9
6. 6 x7
7. 11 x9
8. 8 x8
9. 7 x9
10. 11 x7
11. 11 x9
12. 11 x10
13. 10 x9
14. 11 x11
15. 9 x8
16. 8 x12
17. 10 x9
18. 9 x8
19. 6 x11
20. 8 x7
21. 7 x9
22. 8 x8
23. 12 x10
24. 6 x10
25. 9 x9
26. 10 x11
27. 9 x12
28. 9 x8
29. 10 x9
30. 10 x7
31. 10 x6
32. 10 x10
33. 10 x10
34. 9 x10
35. 7 x9
36. 9 x8
37. 8 x9
38. 11 x8
39. 7 x6
40. 8 x12
41. 9 x10
42. 9 x7
43. 11 x10
44. 10 x8
45. 11 x10
46. 7 x8
47. 12 x7
48. 12 x12
49. 8 x12
50. 10 x11

MULTIPLICATION 6 TO 12

Name: ______________________

Date: __________ Time: __________

Score: /50

1. 12 x12	2. 7 x11	3. 10 x12	4. 8 x10	5. 8 x11
6. 7 x9	7. 9 x9	8. 6 x11	9. 9 x10	10. 10 x6
11. 9 x6	12. 12 x12	13. 10 x9	14. 8 x9	15. 11 x12
16. 8 x11	17. 10 x7	18. 8 x9	19. 9 x11	20. 10 x11
21. 7 x12	22. 7 x10	23. 9 x12	24. 11 x10	25. 7 x10
26. 11 x10	27. 8 x7	28. 11 x11	29. 7 x12	30. 10 x7
31. 8 x10	32. 7 x8	33. 7 x10	34. 11 x7	35. 7 x9
36. 10 x11	37. 8 x8	38. 8 x8	39. 9 x7	40. 9 x11
41. 9 x7	42. 7 x9	43. 8 x11	44. 7 x12	45. 10 x12
46. 7 x9	47. 9 x11	48. 12 x10	49. 12 x7	50. 10 x8

MULTIPLY THE NUMBERS

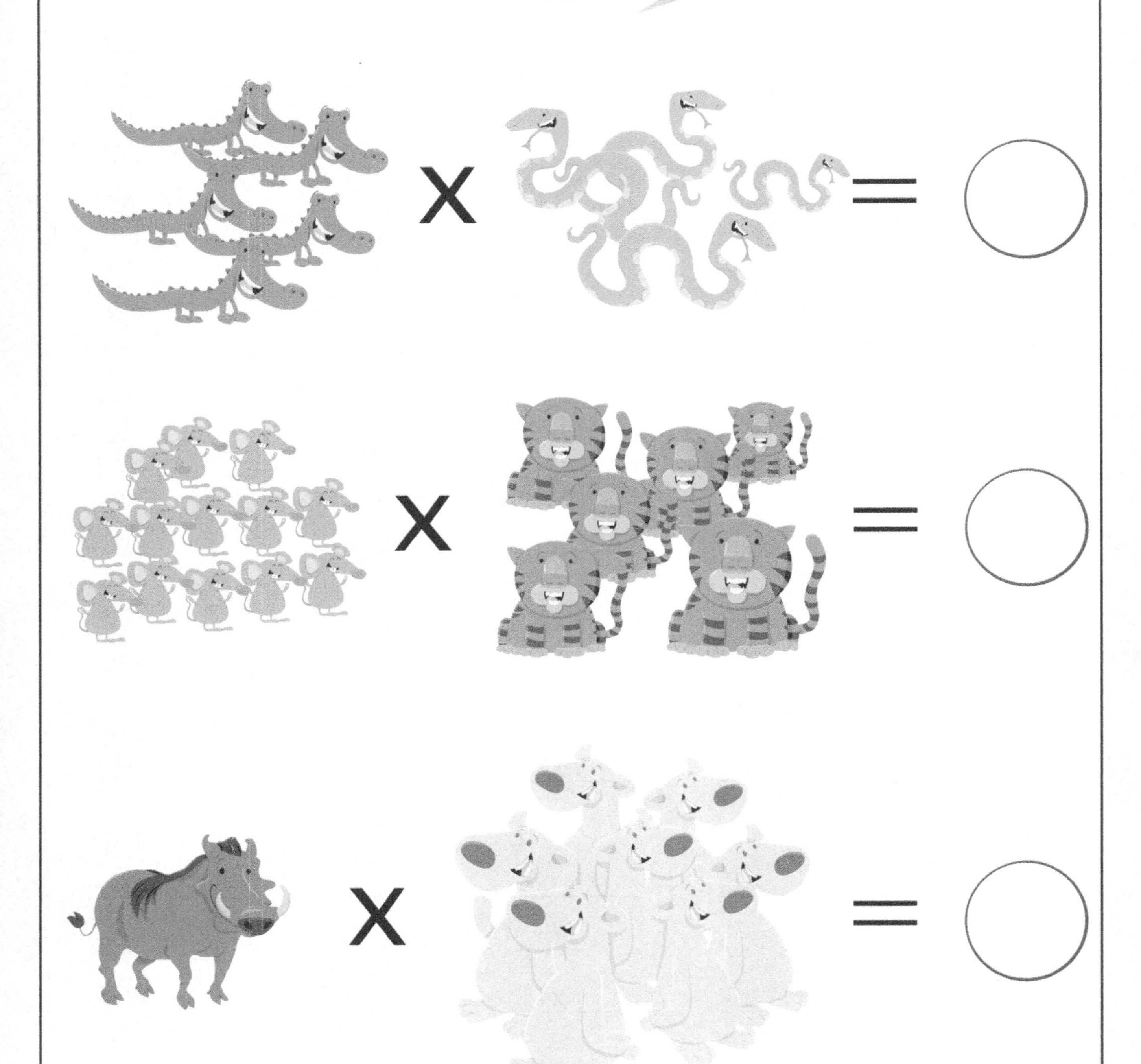

Name: ____________________

Date: __________ Time: __________

WORD PROBLEMS

ADDITION 11 TO 15

1. Liam places 6 tomatoes in each basket. There are 4 baskets. How many tomatoes are there?

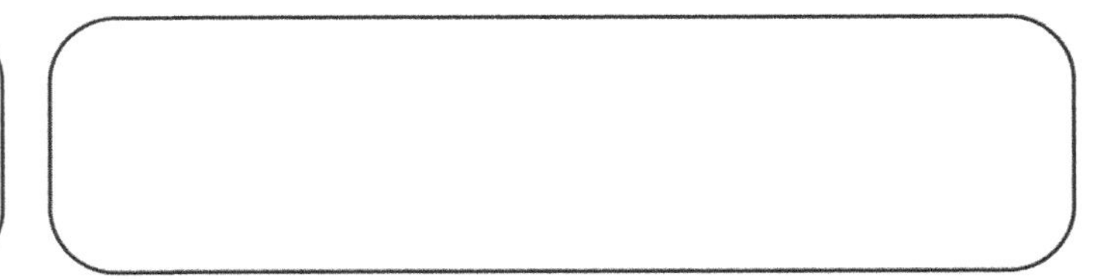

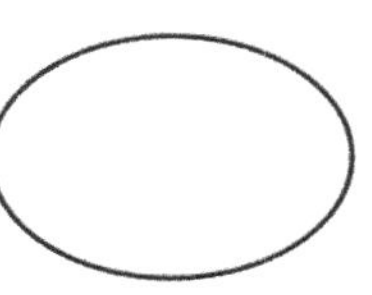

Answer

2. There are 7 toys in a shelf. How many toys are there in 3 shelves?

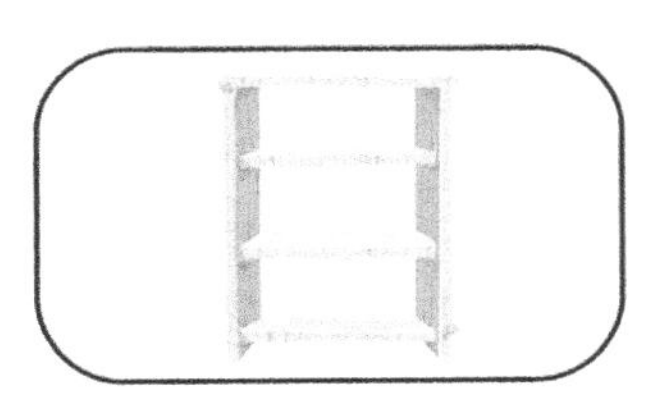

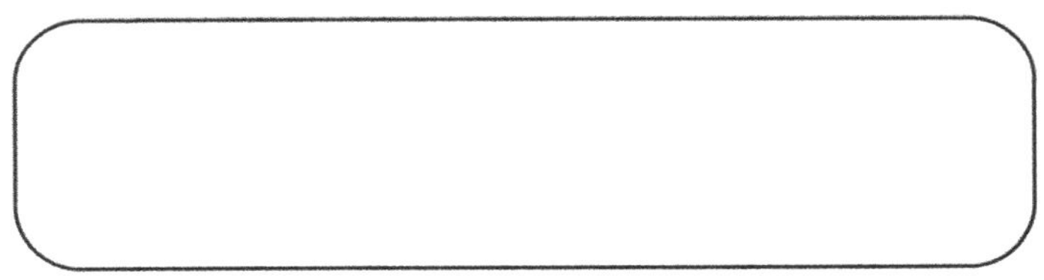

Answer

3. There are 6 ornaments in a box. How many ornaments are there in 10 boxes?

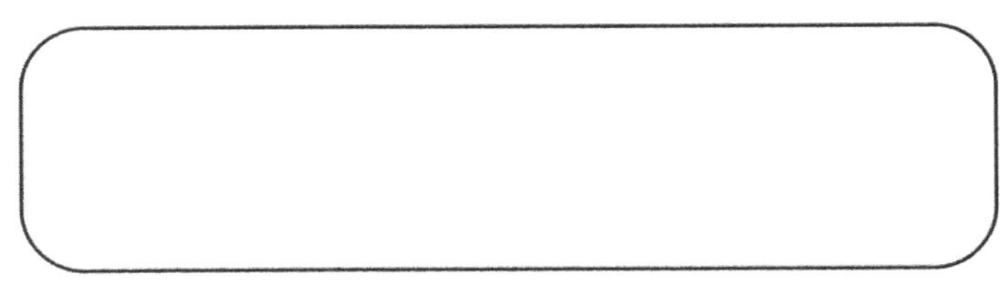

Answer

4. Jade arranges chairs in 8 rows. There are 4 chairs in each row. How many chairs are there altogether?

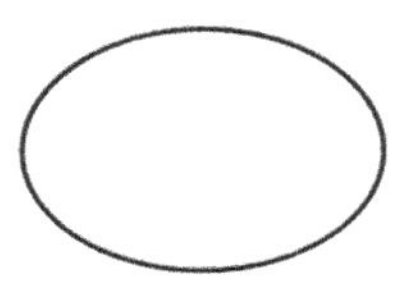

Answer

WORD PROBLEMS
MULTIPLICATION 6 TO 12

Name: ____________________

Date: __________ Time: __________

5. Wendy arranges 9 tiles in a row. There are 8 rows. How many tiles are there?

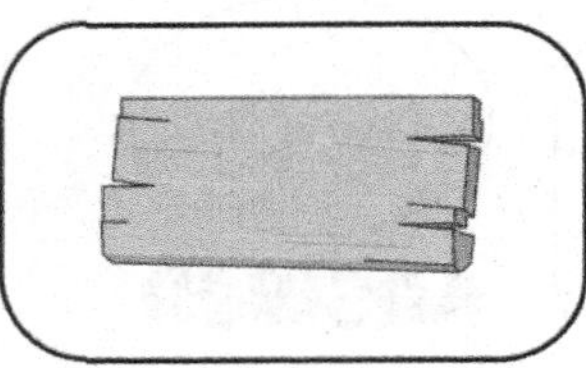

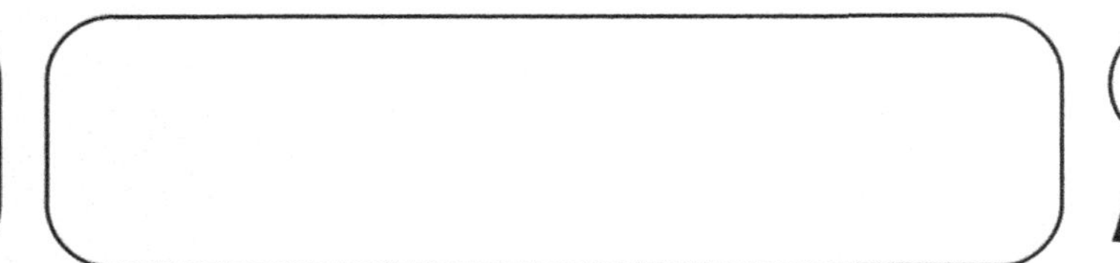

ANSWER

6. There are 10 water bottles in the fridge, and there are thrice that many water bottles in the storeroom. How many water bottles are there in the storeroom?

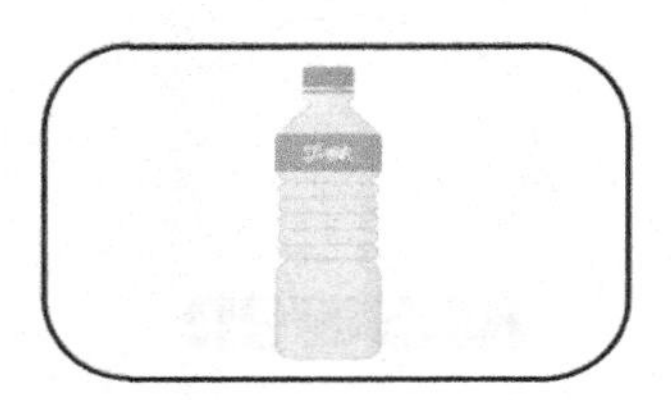

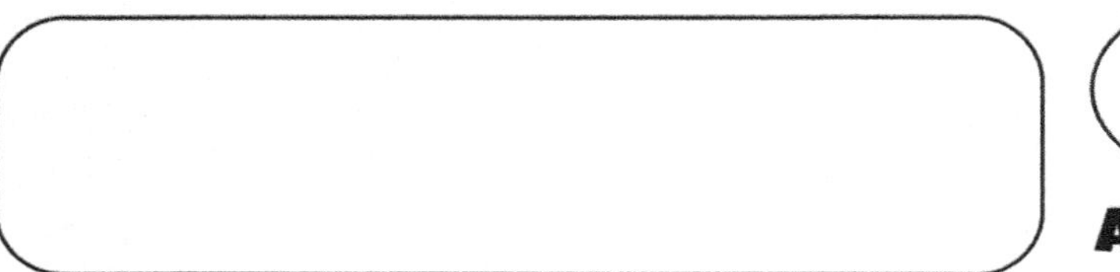

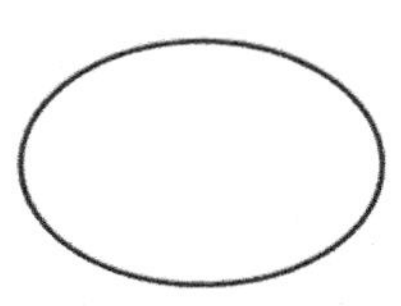

ANSWER

7. There are 5 children in a group. How many children are there in 11 groups?

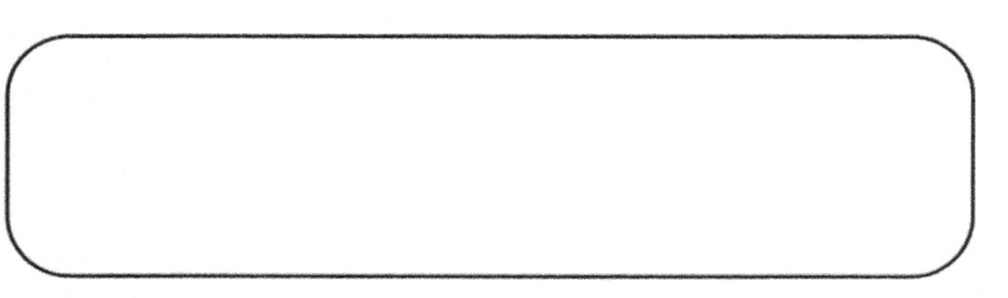

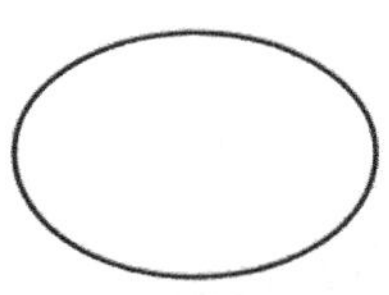

ANSWER

8. Ruby has 7 skirts and twice as many shirts. How many shirts does Ruby have?

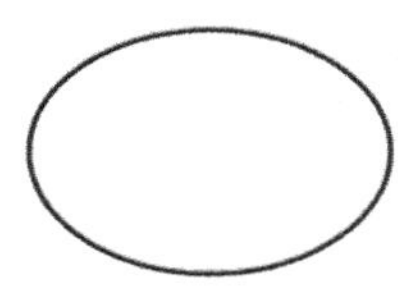

ANSWER

WORD PROBLEMS
MULTIPLICATION 6 TO 12

Name: ____________________

Date: __________ Time: __________

9. Noel has 12 papers in a stack. He has 10 stacks of papers. How many papers does Noel have?

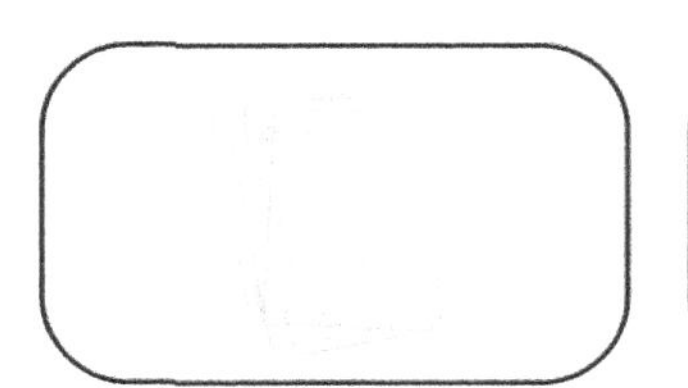  

ANSWER

10. If a juice box costs $2, how much will 9 juice boxes cost?

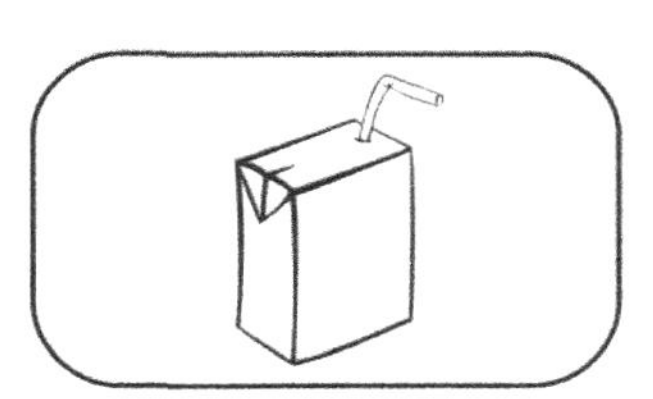 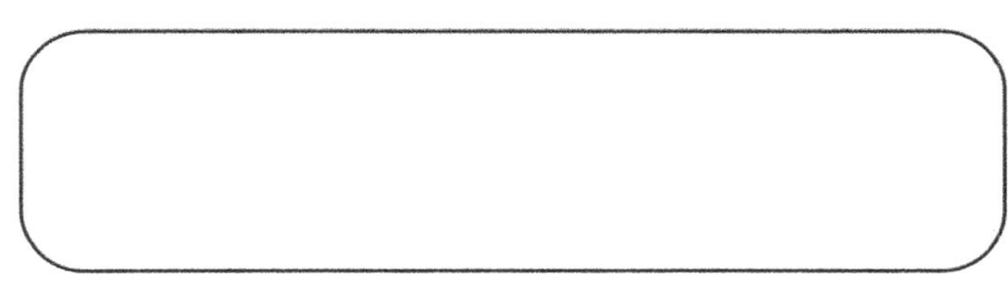 

ANSWER

11. Ben wrote 7 short stories. Piper wrote 3 times as many short stories. How many short stories did Piper write?

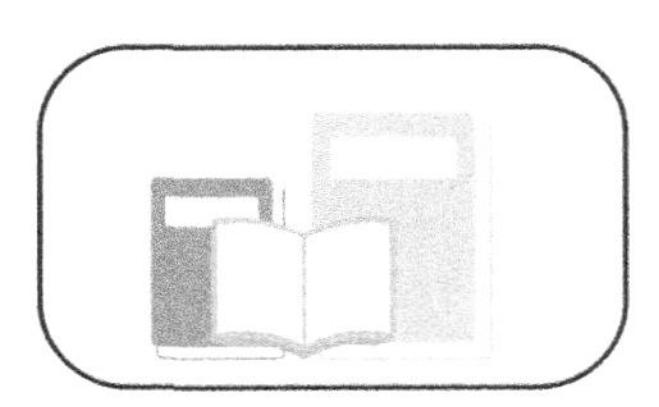 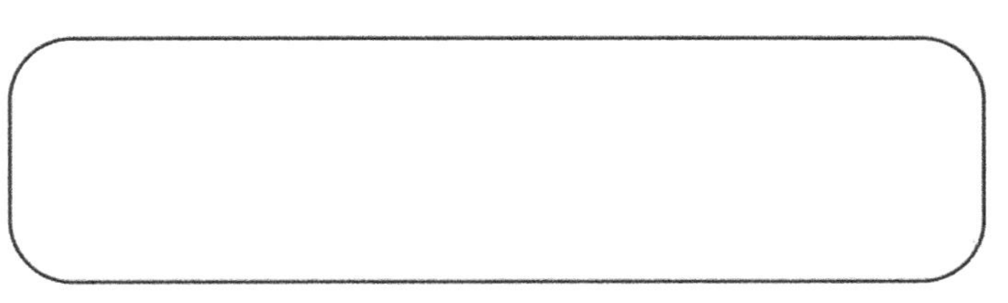 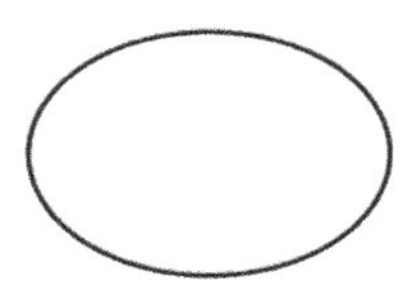

ANSWER

12. There are 10 markers in the small box and 7 times that many in the large box. How many markers are in the large box?

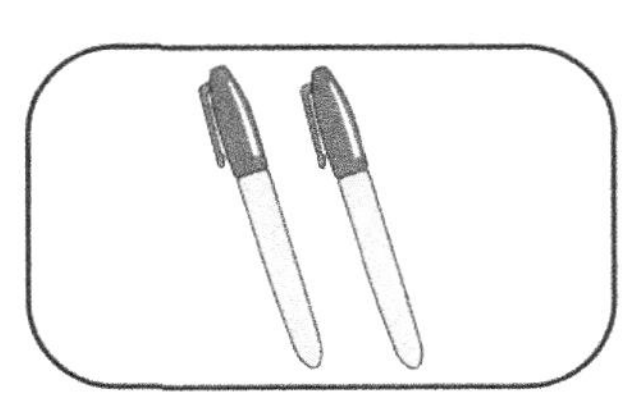 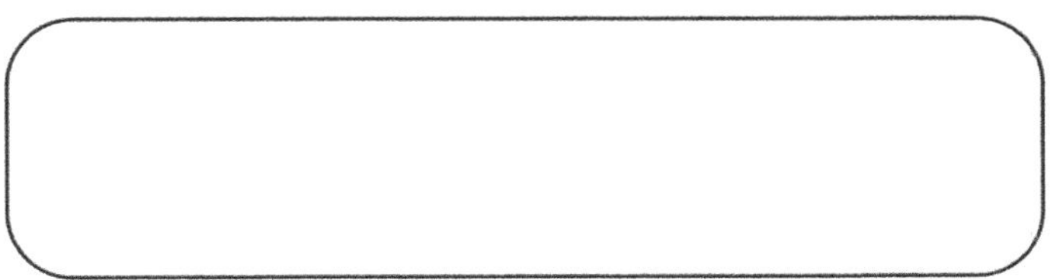 

ANSWER

ACTIVITY CORNER

COLORING ACTIVITY

WORD PROBLEMS
MULTIPLICATION 6 TO 12

Name: ____________________

Date: __________ Time: __________

13. Sam wrote 7 poems. Miles wrote 5 times as many poems. How many poems did Miles write?

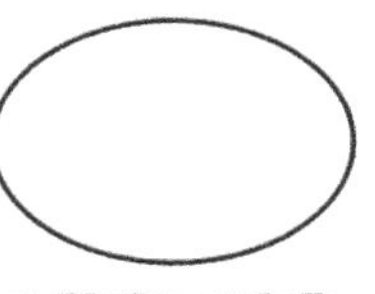

Answer

14. There are 9 quilts in the first exhibit and 4 times that many in the second exhibit. How many quilts are in the second exhibit?

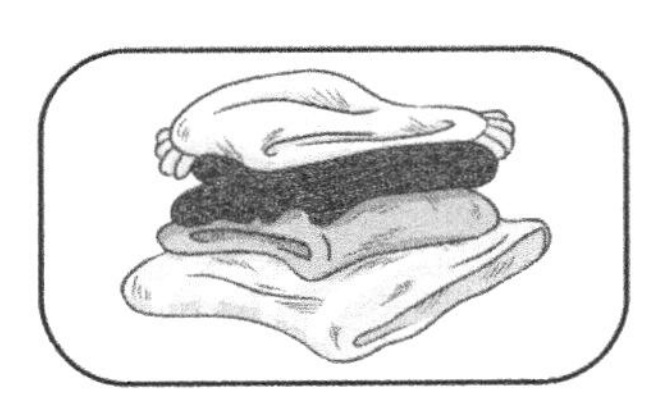
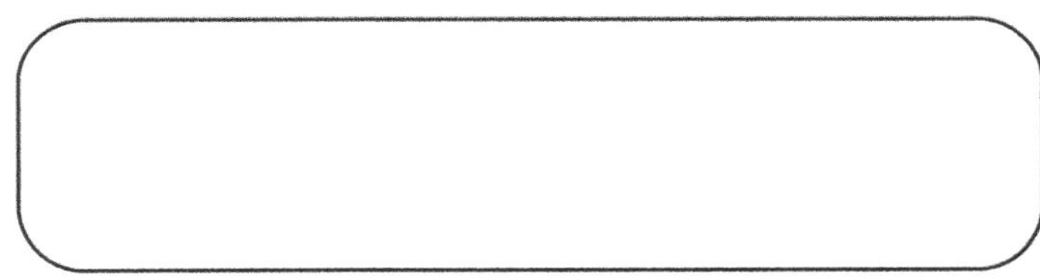
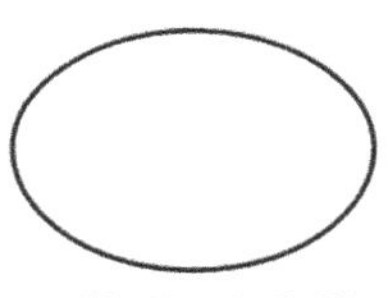

Answer

15. May has 10 roses. Luna has 4 times as many roses. How many roses does Luna have?

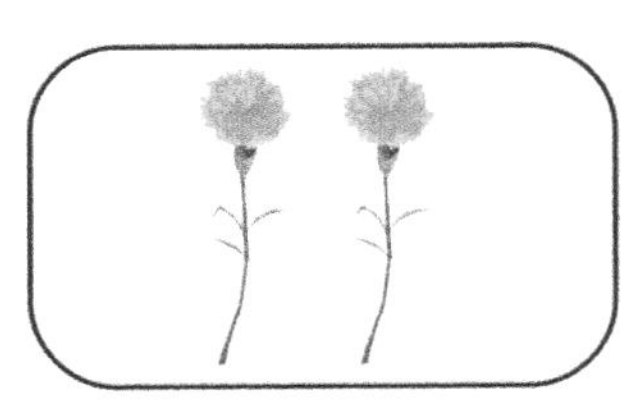
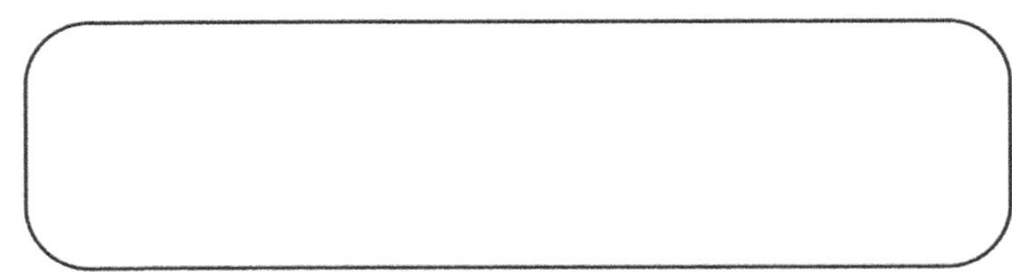
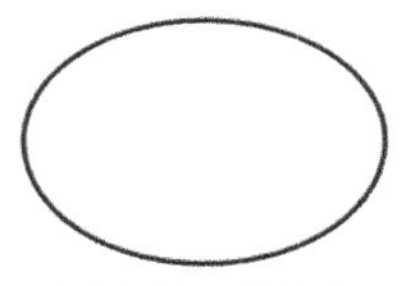

Answer

16. There are 6 books on the small table and 2 times that many on the big table. How many books are on the big table?

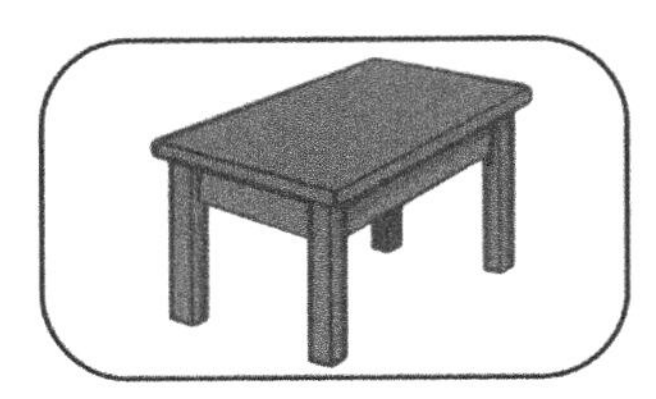

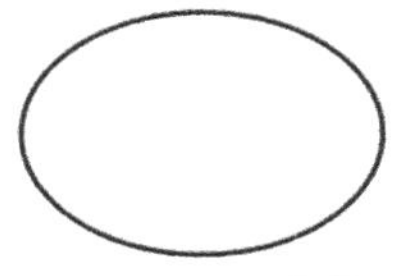

Answer

WORD PROBLEMS
MULTIPLICATION 6 TO 12

Name: ____________________

Date: __________ Time: __________

17. Zach picked up 8 pieces of trash. Ella picked up 3 times as many pieces of trash. How many pieces of trash did Ella pick up?

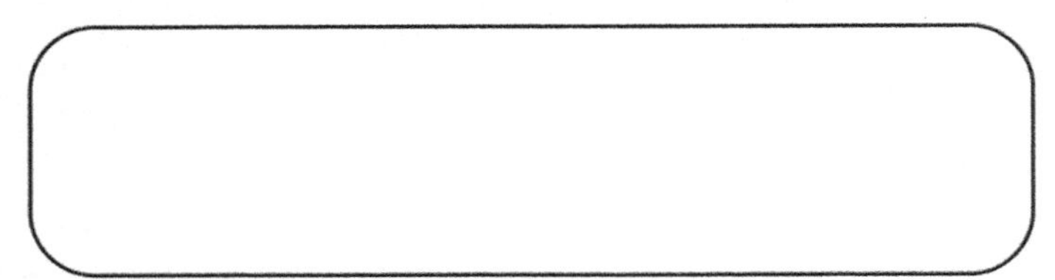

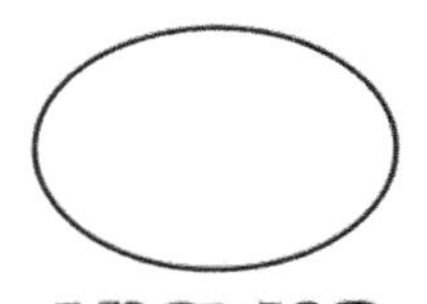

Answer

18. There are 11 fourth graders in the green group and 2 times that many in the red group. How many fourth graders are in the red group?

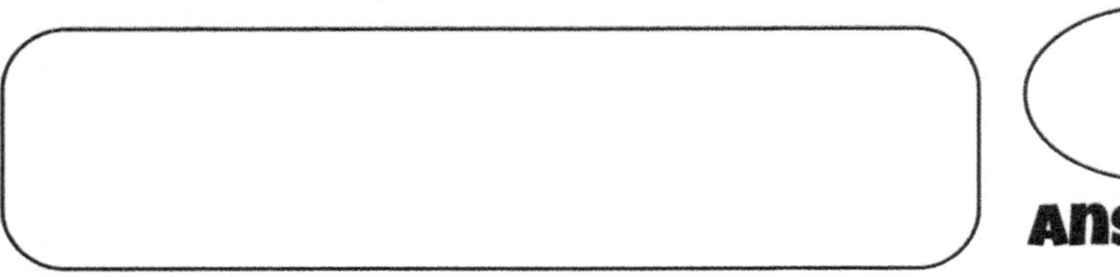

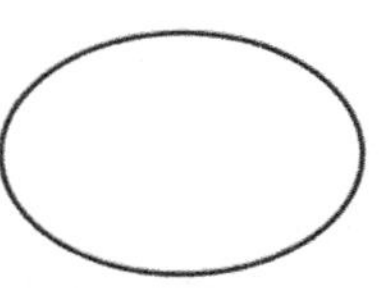

Answer

19. There are 7 computers downstairs and 7 times that many computers upstairs. How many computers are upstairs?

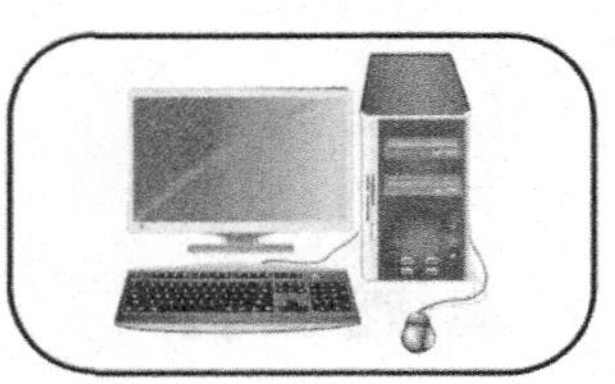

Answer

20. There are 9 nickels in the red can and 7 times that many in the green can. How many nickels are in the green can?

Answer

WORD PROBLEMS
MULTIPLICATION 6 TO 12

Name: ____________________

Date: __________ Time: __________

21. Julie has 8 pounds of grapes in each container. She has 4 containers. How much grapes does she have altogether?

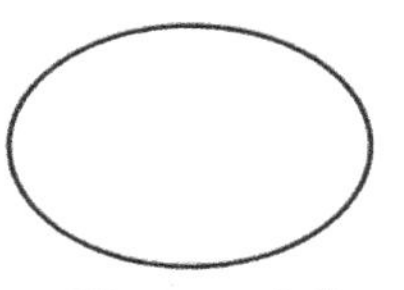

ANSWER

22. Luke baked 6 pies, and Jack baked 5 times as many pies as Luke. How many pies did Jack bake?

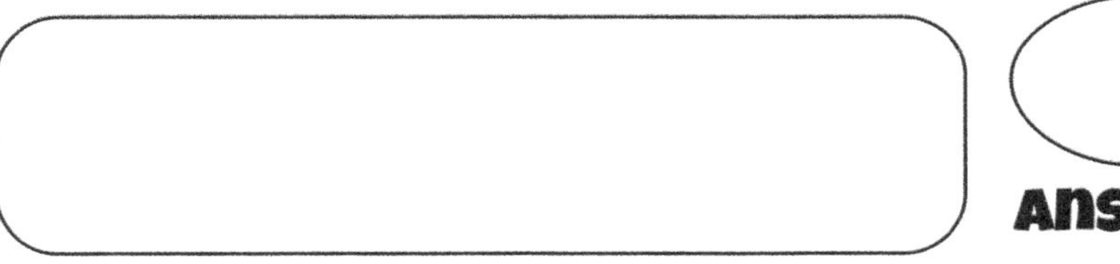

ANSWER

23. A toy costs $8. How much do 11 toys cost?

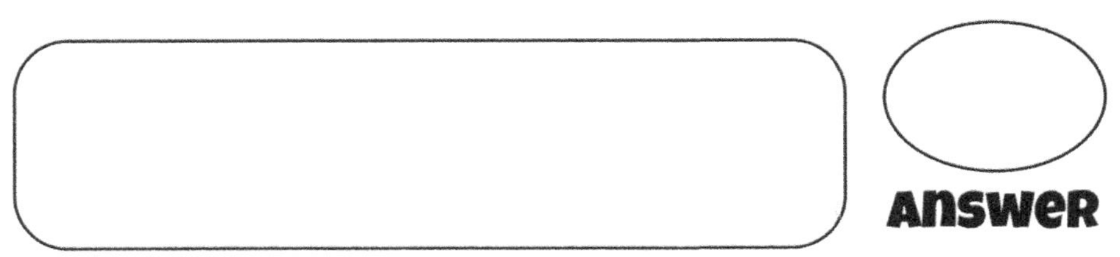

ANSWER

24. There are 12 vegetables in a basket. How many vegetables are there in 5 baskets?

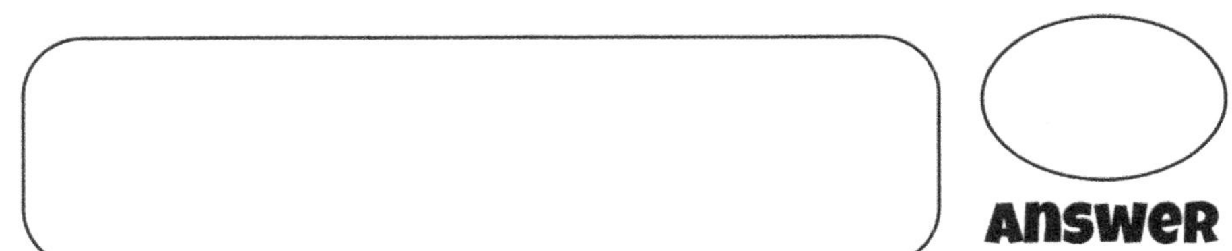

ANSWER

WORD PROBLEMS
MULTIPLICATION 6 TO 12

Name: ____________________

Date: __________ Time: __________

25. Ned drives 10 miles an hour. How many miles does he drive in 4 hours?

ANSWER

ACTIVITY CORNER

CONNECT THE DOTS

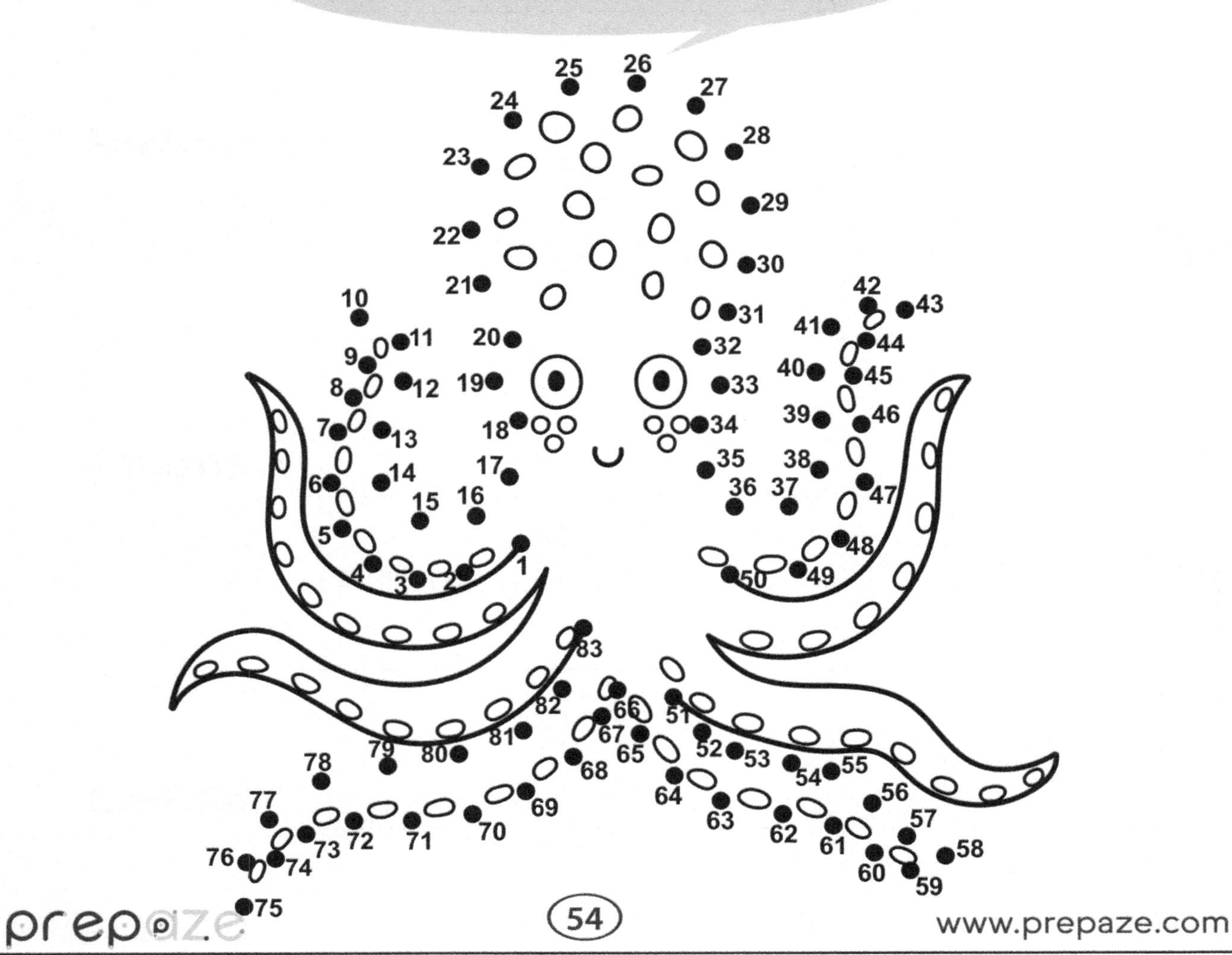

MULTIPLICATION 9 TO 12

Name: ______________________

Date: __________ Time: __________

Score: /50

1. 10 x10	2. 12 x10	3. 12 x10	4. 12 x11	5. 11 x10
6. 11 x10	7. 12 x12	8. 10 x12	9. 10 x12	10. 9 x10
11. 10 x9	12. 10 x12	13. 11 x11	14. 11 x12	15. 9 x9
16. 11 x12	17. 11 x11	18. 10 x10	19. 12 x11	20. 9 x10
21. 10 x9	22. 11 x10	23. 11 x9	24. 10 x11	25. 10 x10
26. 12 x11	27. 10 x10	28. 10 x11	29. 12 x10	30. 9 x10
31. 12 x11	32. 11 x10	33. 11 x12	34. 11 x10	35. 12 x11
36. 9 x11	37. 9 x11	38. 10 x11	39. 9 x9	40. 12 x9
41. 10 x10	42. 12 x11	43. 10 x10	44. 11 x10	45. 10 x10
46. 11 x9	47. 9 x11	48. 10 x9	49. 11 x12	50. 11 x11

MULTIPLICATION 9 TO 12

Name: ______________________

Date: __________ Time: __________

Score: /50

1. 11 x11	2. 10 x10	3. 10 x11	4. 11 x10	5. 9 x11
6. 10 x11	7. 10 x11	8. 9 x11	9. 10 x12	10. 10 x11
11. 10 x10	12. 11 x10	13. 11 x10	14. 11 x11	15. 9 x11
16. 9 x10	17. 10 x10	18. 9 x9	19. 10 x9	20. 9 x10
21. 12 x11	22. 10 x9	23. 11 x11	24. 10 x12	25. 12 x12
26. 10 x12	27. 10 x9	28. 10 x10	29. 11 x9	30. 12 x12
31. 12 x11	32. 11 x11	33. 10 x11	34. 9 x10	35. 10 x12
36. 10 x12	37. 11 x11	38. 10 x10	39. 11 x11	40. 12 x10
41. 11 x12	42. 12 x12	43. 11 x12	44. 10 x11	45. 10 x11
46. 9 x10	47. 12 x11	48. 11 x10	49. 10 x10	50. 10 x12

MULTIPLICATION 9 TO 12

Name: ____________ Date: ________ Time: ________

Score: /50

1. 11 x10	2. 12 x10	3. 11 x11	4. 11 x11	5. 9 x10
6. 11 x9	7. 11 x11	8. 12 x11	9. 9 x12	10. 11 x10
11. 9 x11	12. 11 x11	13. 11 x12	14. 9 x12	15. 11 x10
16. 10 x10	17. 11 x10	18. 11 x11	19. 11 x12	20. 11 x10
21. 9 x10	22. 12 x9	23. 12 x12	24. 10 x9	25. 10 x11
26. 11 x10	27. 10 x11	28. 12 x10	29. 10 x12	30. 9 x10
31. 9 x12	32. 11 x9	33. 10 x12	34. 11 x11	35. 11 x9
36. 9 x9	37. 12 x11	38. 10 x9	39. 10 x11	40. 10 x9
41. 10 x9	42. 11 x9	43. 10 x10	44. 11 x12	45. 12 x10
46. 9 x11	47. 11 x12	48. 9 x10	49. 11 x10	50. 10 x10

MULTIPLICATION 9 TO 12

Name: ______________________

Date: __________ Time: __________

Score: /50

1. 11 x10	2. 10 x9	3. 11 x10	4. 9 x12	5. 11 x11
6. 11 x11	7. 9 x11	8. 11 x11	9. 10 x10	10. 10 x11
11. 10 x10	12. 11 x9	13. 11 x10	14. 11 x11	15. 9 x11
16. 11 x10	17. 9 x10	18. 12 x9	19. 10 x11	20. 11 x10
21. 12 x9	22. 11 x10	23. 11 x10	24. 9 x9	25. 10 x11
26. 9 x12	27. 10 x10	28. 11 x11	29. 10 x9	30. 10 x12
31. 10 x12	32. 12 x11	33. 11 x11	34. 9 x11	35. 11 x9
36. 10 x11	37. 11 x10	38. 11 x9	39. 11 x10	40. 11 x10
41. 11 x11	42. 10 x9	43. 11 x10	44. 10 x11	45. 11 x11
46. 9 x12	47. 9 x11	48. 10 x9	49. 10 x11	50. 10 x12

MULTIPLICATION 9 TO 12

Name: ____________________

Date: __________ Time: __________

Score: /50

1. 10 x10	2. 12 x9	3. 10 x11	4. 11 x10	5. 11 x11
6. 11 x11	7. 12 x10	8. 11 x11	9. 12 x12	10. 11 x10
11. 10 x12	12. 10 x11	13. 11 x10	14. 10 x9	15. 11 x11
16. 11 x10	17. 10 x12	18. 10 x9	19. 12 x11	20. 11 x10
21. 10 x9	22. 12 x9	23. 11 x10	24. 11 x12	25. 10 x12
26. 10 x11	27. 10 x12	28. 11 x9	29. 12 x12	30. 11 x12
31. 11 x12	32. 10 x11	33. 10 x10	34. 9 x10	35. 9 x9
36. 10 x10	37. 10 x10	38. 12 x12	39. 9 x10	40. 11 x12
41. 12 x12	42. 10 x11	43. 11 x11	44. 10 x12	45. 9 x11
46. 11 x10	47. 9 x10	48. 11 x11	49. 10 x11	50. 11 x9

MULTIPLICATION 9 TO 12

Name: ____________________

Date: __________ Time: __________

Score: /50

1. 12 x10	2. 12 x10	3. 9 x11	4. 12 x11	5. 11 x10
6. 12 x12	7. 9 x11	8. 10 x11	9. 10 x11	10. 10 x9
11. 10 x10	12. 9 x10	13. 11 x12	14. 9 x12	15. 11 x10
16. 11 x10	17. 9 x9	18. 10 x11	19. 10 x10	20. 12 x12
21. 9 x11	22. 10 x10	23. 10 x10	24. 10 x11	25. 11 x12
26. 11 x10	27. 12 x9	28. 12 x11	29. 9 x11	30. 10 x10
31. 11 x10	32. 12 x11	33. 10 x12	34. 10 x10	35. 10 x9
36. 11 x11	37. 9 x12	38. 12 x11	39. 12 x10	40. 12 x10
41. 9 x11	42. 11 x9	43. 9 x11	44. 9 x11	45. 12 x12
46. 11 x11	47. 11 x9	48. 10 x11	49. 10 x10	50. 11 x12

MULTIPLICATION 9 TO 12

Name: ____________________

Date: __________ Time: __________

Score: /50

1. 11 x11	2. 9 x12	3. 11 x11	4. 10 x10	5. 12 x10
6. 12 x11	7. 12 x12	8. 11 x10	9. 11 x9	10. 9 x10
11. 11 x11	12. 9 x12	13. 10 x11	14. 9 x11	15. 10 x12
16. 9 x10	17. 10 x12	18. 11 x10	19. 11 x11	20. 12 x10
21. 12 x10	22. 10 x9	23. 12 x10	24. 11 x11	25. 9 x12
26. 12 x11	27. 12 x12	28. 12 x9	29. 10 x9	30. 10 x11
31. 12 x9	32. 10 x9	33. 10 x11	34. 12 x11	35. 10 x9
36. 11 x12	37. 12 x10	38. 10 x12	39. 11 x10	40. 10 x10
41. 12 x11	42. 10 x11	43. 10 x11	44. 9 x12	45. 11 x11
46. 11 x11	47. 11 x11	48. 10 x11	49. 11 x11	50. 12 x11

MULTIPLICATION 9 TO 12

Name: ____________________

Date: __________ Time: __________

Score: /50

1. 11 x9	2. 12 x10	3. 11 x10	4. 10 x12	5. 11 x11
6. 12 x10	7. 11 x11	8. 11 x11	9. 12 x12	10. 9 x11
11. 11 x10	12. 11 x11	13. 11 x11	14. 11 x10	15. 11 x10
16. 10 x10	17. 10 x11	18. 12 x9	19. 10 x11	20. 11 x10
21. 11 x11	22. 12 x12	23. 12 x9	24. 11 x12	25. 10 x11
26. 12 x12	27. 9 x11	28. 9 x10	29. 10 x11	30. 10 x12
31. 11 x10	32. 10 x11	33. 11 x10	34. 9 x9	35. 11 x12
36. 12 x11	37. 11 x10	38. 12 x10	39. 9 x10	40. 11 x11
41. 10 x10	42. 10 x12	43. 9 x10	44. 11 x12	45. 11 x12
46. 12 x10	47. 11 x10	48. 9 x10	49. 12 x11	50. 10 x12

WORD PROBLEMS
MULTIPLICATION 9 TO 12

Name: ______________________

Date: __________ Time: __________

1. Phoebe has a star. Kiara had 3 times as many stars. How many stars does Kiara have?

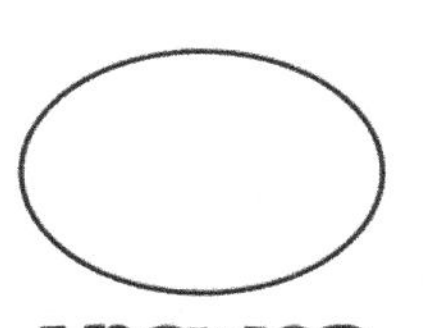

Answer

2. Simon has 2 dogs and twice as many cats. How many cats does Simon have?

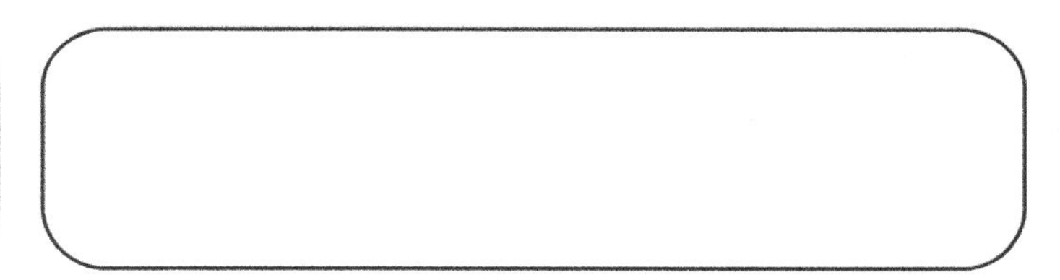
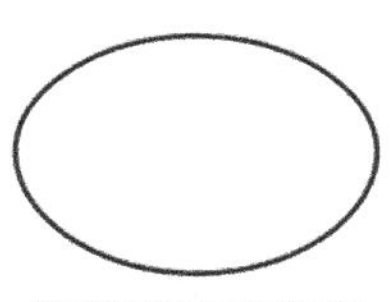

Answer

3. There are 2 windows in a room. How many windows are there in 3 rooms?

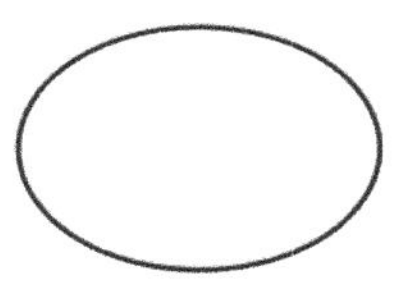

Answer

4. There are 4 apples in a box. How many apples are there in 4 boxes?

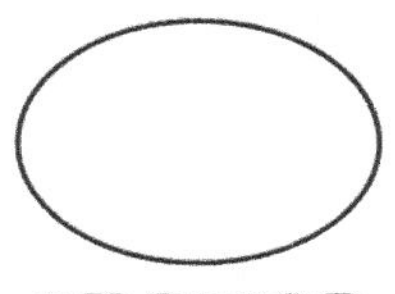

Answer

WORD PROBLEMS
MULTIPLICATION 9 TO 12

Name: ____________________

Date: __________ Time: __________

5. There are 3 people on each park bench. How many people are there in 4 park benches?

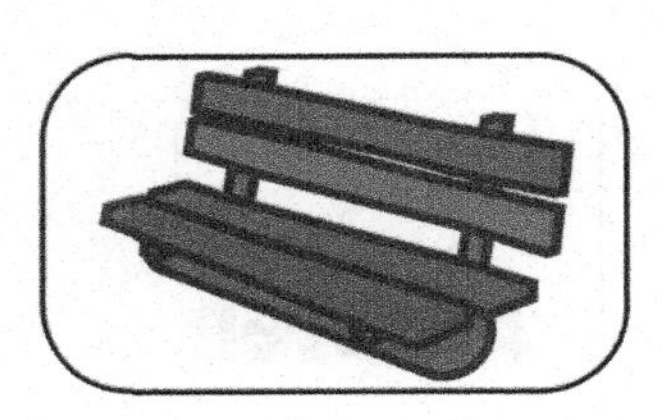

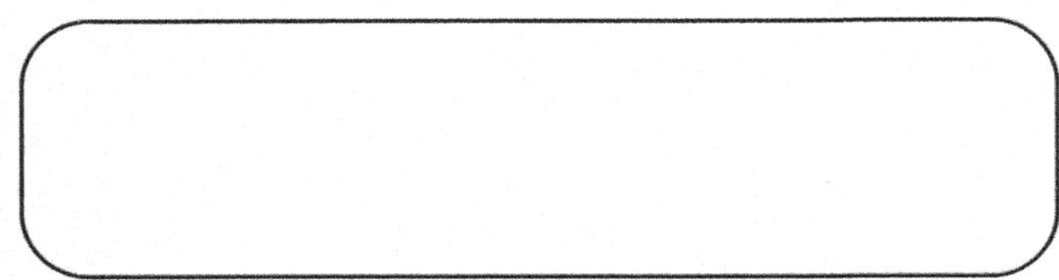

ANSWER

6. Cole makes 2 toasts for himself. He makes 4 times as many toasts for others. How many toasts does he make for others?

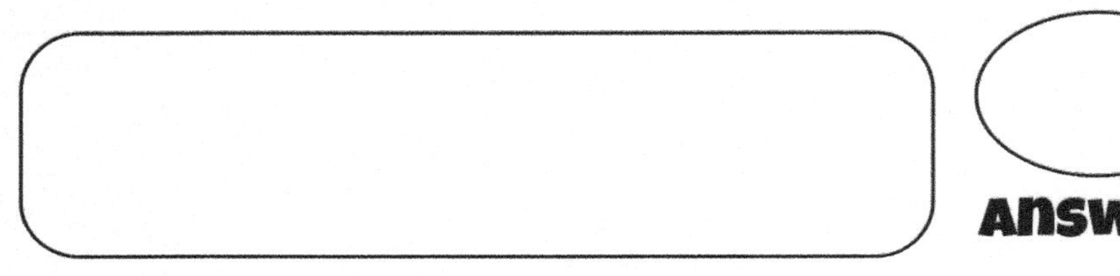

ANSWER

7. A horse has 4 legs. How many legs do 5 horses have?

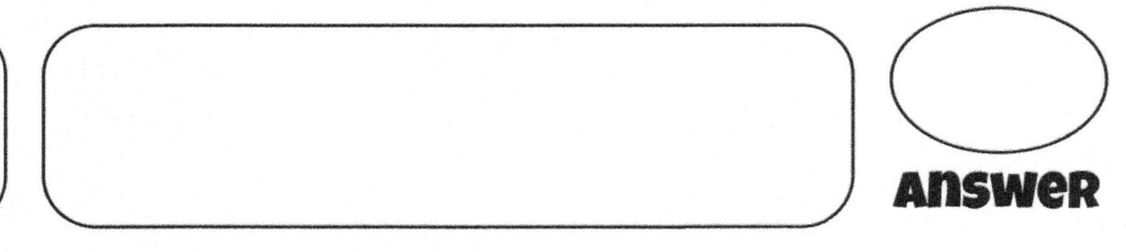

ANSWER

8. There are 8 sticky notes on each board. How many sticky notes are there on 10 boards?

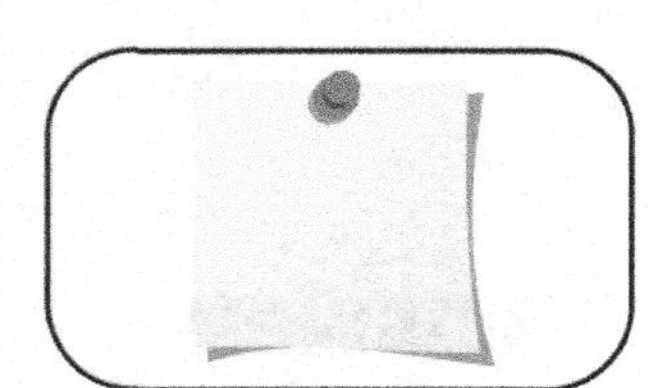

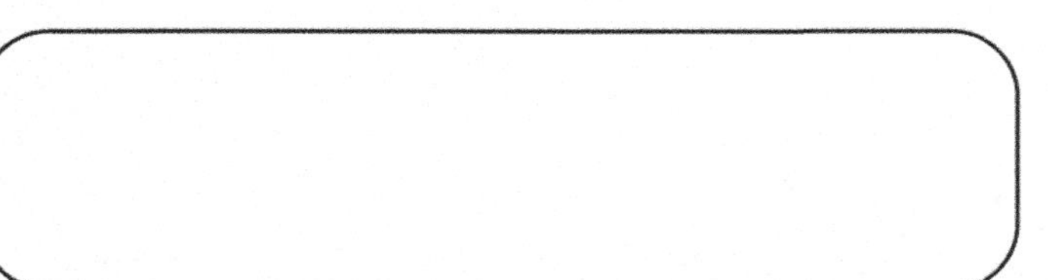

ANSWER

WORD PROBLEMS
MULTIPLICATION 9 TO 12

Name: ______________________

Date: __________ Time: __________

9. Tom colors 9 shapes. Darla colors 5 times as many shapes as Tom. How many shapes does Darla color?

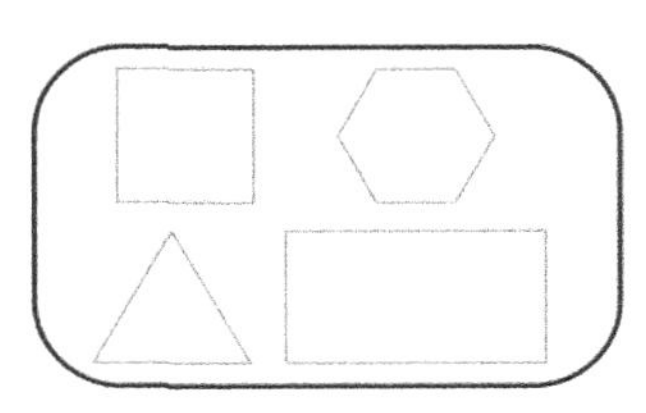
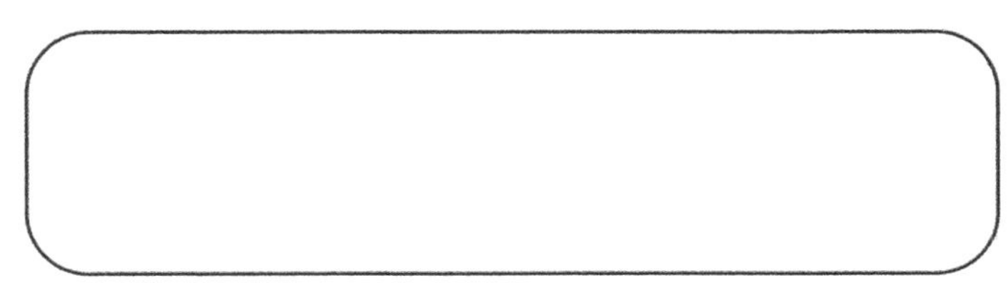

ANSWER

10. A classroom has 10 tables. How many tables are there in 9 classrooms?

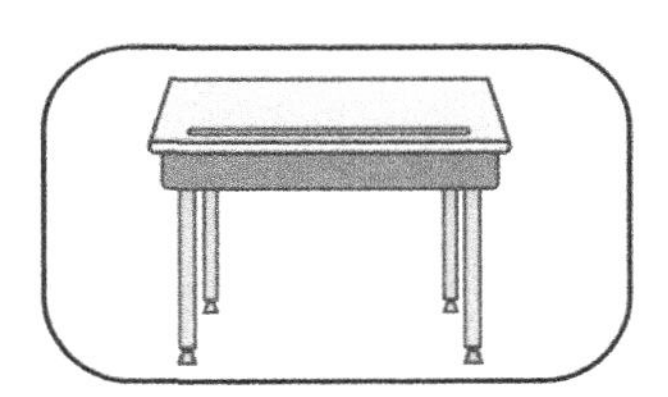

ANSWER

11. There are 5 toes in each foot. How many toes are there in 10 feet?

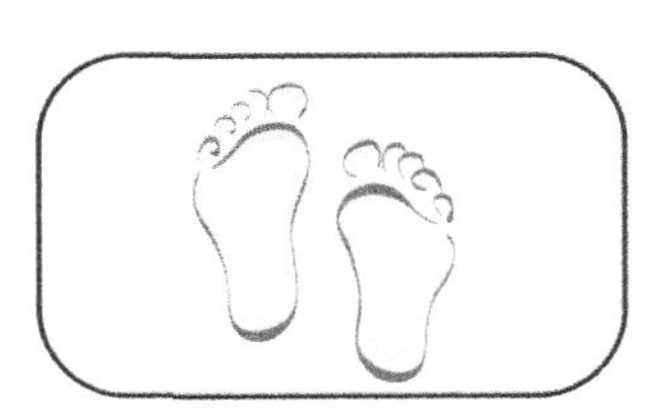
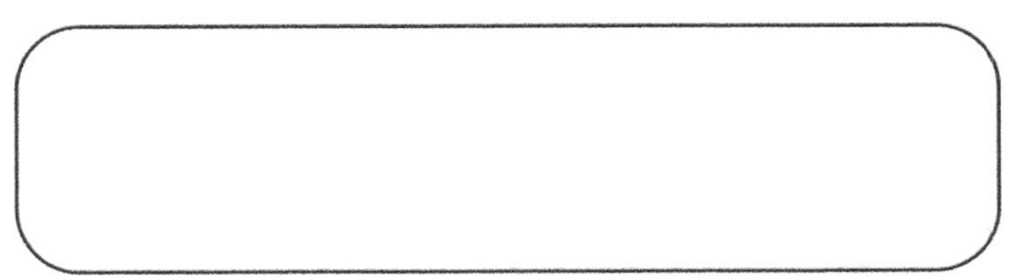
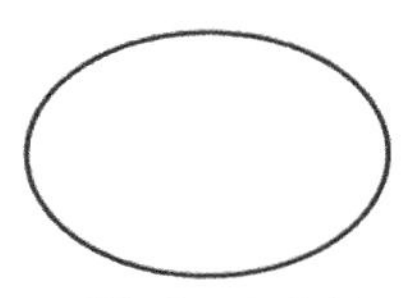

ANSWER

12. Henry has 12 games, and his sister has twice as many games on her computer. How many games does Henry's sister have?

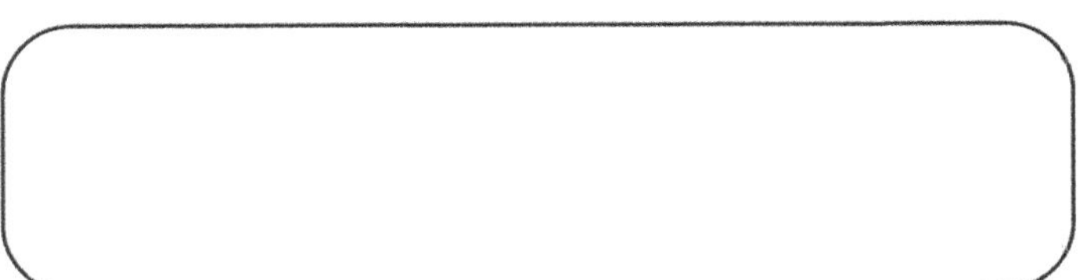
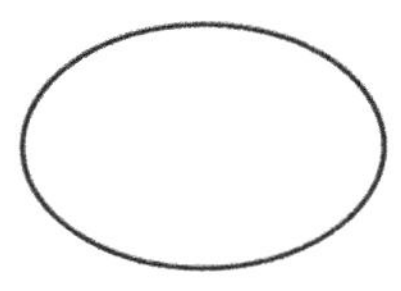

ANSWER

MULTIPLY THE NUMBERS

2 x 12 = ___

5 x 8 = ___

10 x 9 = ___

WORD PROBLEMS
MULTIPLICATION 9 TO 12

Name: ______________________

Date: __________ Time: __________

13. There are 4 people in each car. How many people are there in 9 cars?

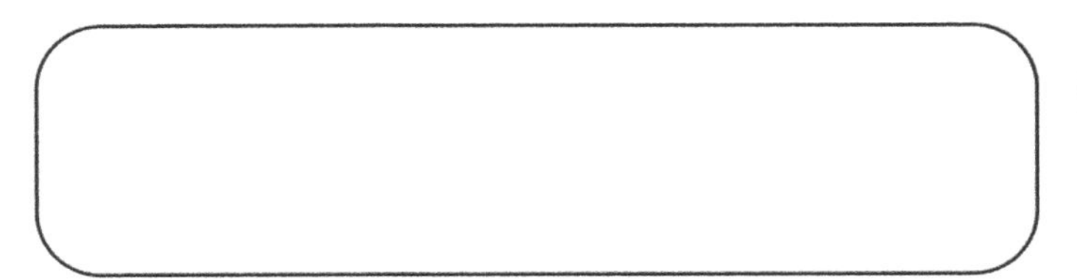

Answer

14. There are 8 lions in a zoo. There are twice as many gorillas. How many gorillas are there in the zoo?

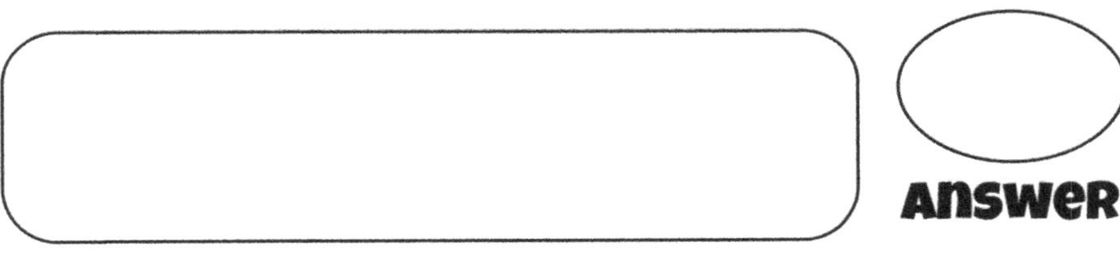

Answer

15. Nick downloads 5 songs each day for a week. How many songs does he download?

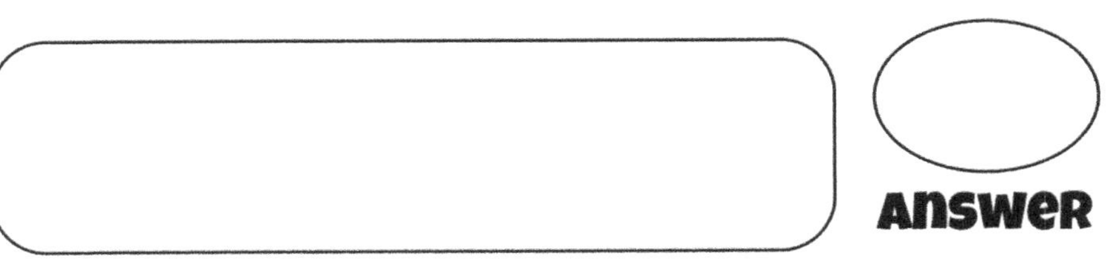

Answer

16. There are 5 mugs in each tray. There are 9 trays. How many mugs are there?

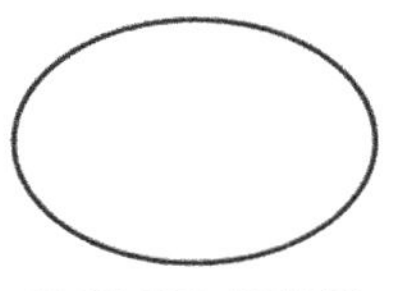

Answer

WORD PROBLEMS
MULTIPLICATION 9 TO 12

Name: ______________________

Date: __________ Time: __________

17. There are 8 pencils in a box. How many pencils are there in 9 boxes?

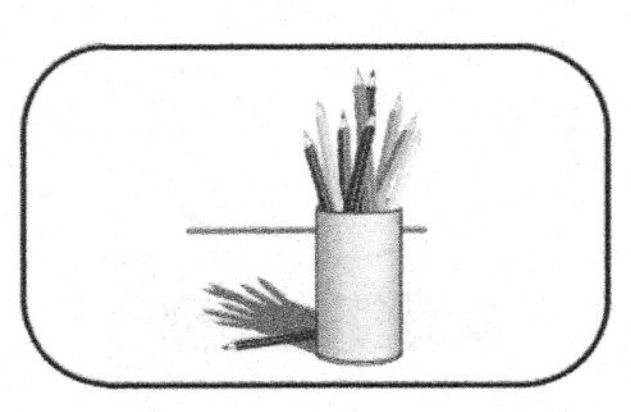

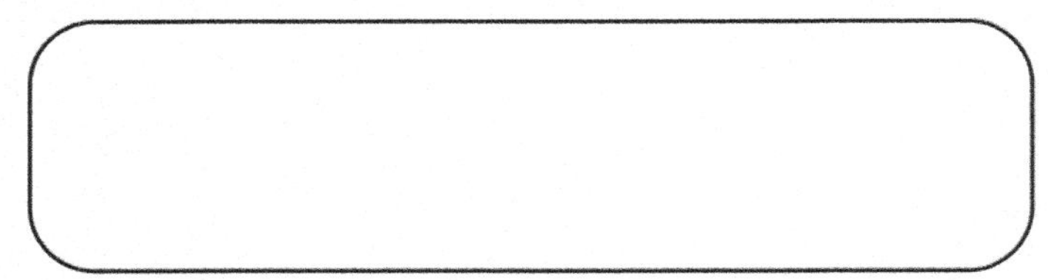

ANSWER

18. There are 6 popsicles in a container. How many popsicles are there in 10 containers?

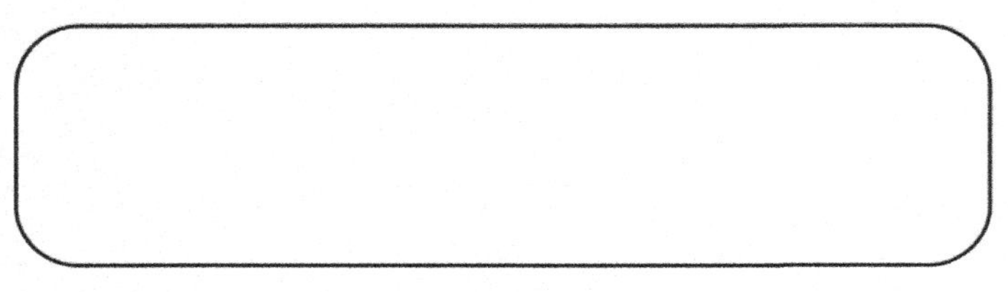

ANSWER

19. Nail rehearses for 4 weeks. How many days does Nail rehearse?

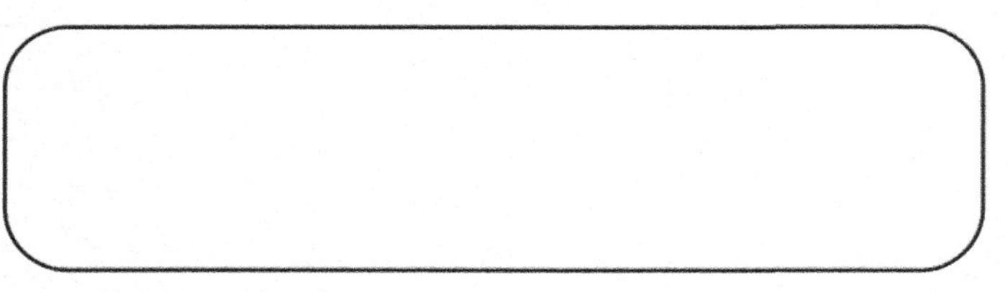

ANSWER

20. There are 6 erasers in a box. How many erasers are there in 11 boxes?

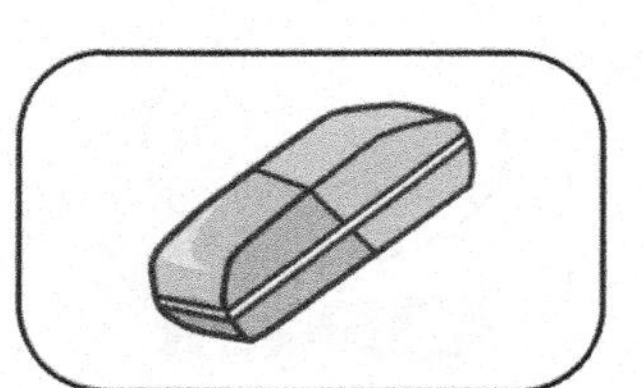

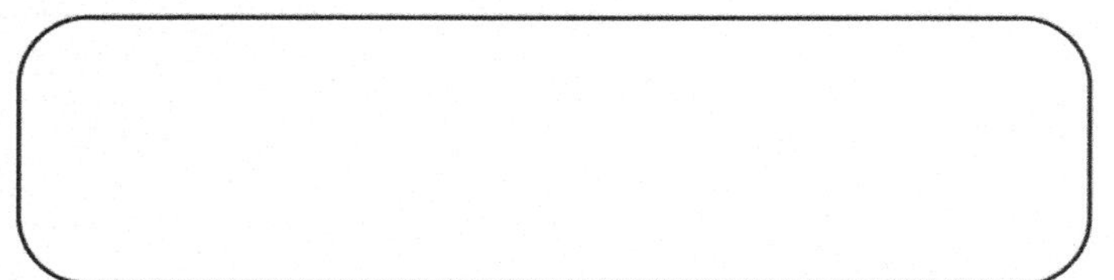

ANSWER

WORD PROBLEMS
MULTIPLICATION 9 TO 12

Name: ____________________
Date: __________ Time: __________

21. Stella has 3 playlists. Each playlist has 12 songs. How many songs arethere in the 3 playlists?

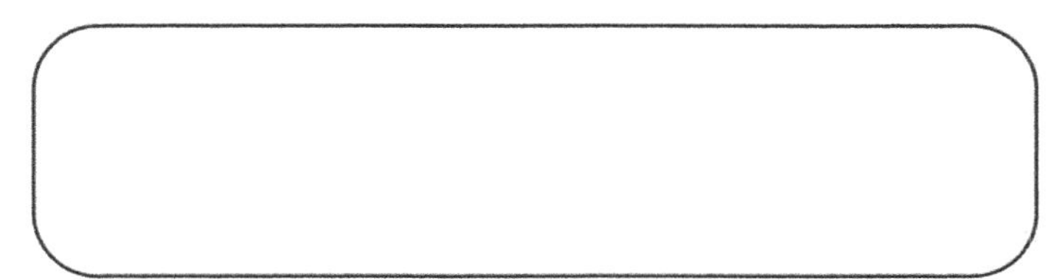

Answer

22. Ian has 9 cards, and Riley has 7 times as many cards as Ian. How many cards does Riley have?

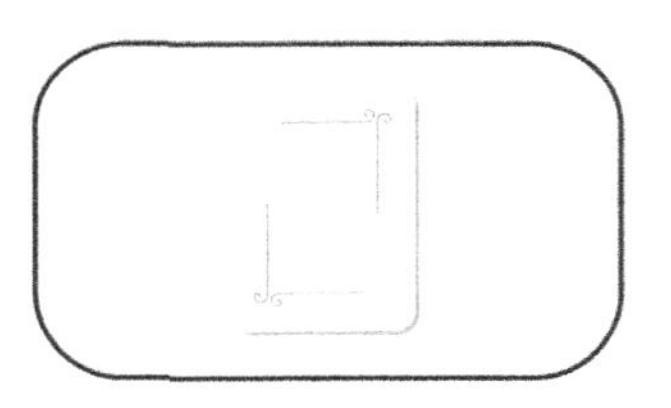
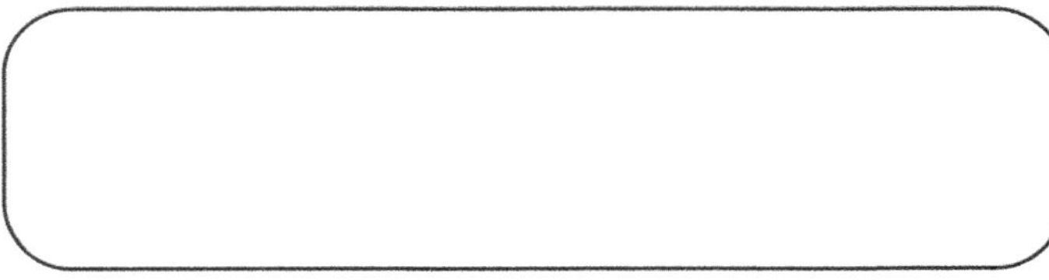

Answer

23. There are 8 people on a boat. How many people are there on 8 boats?

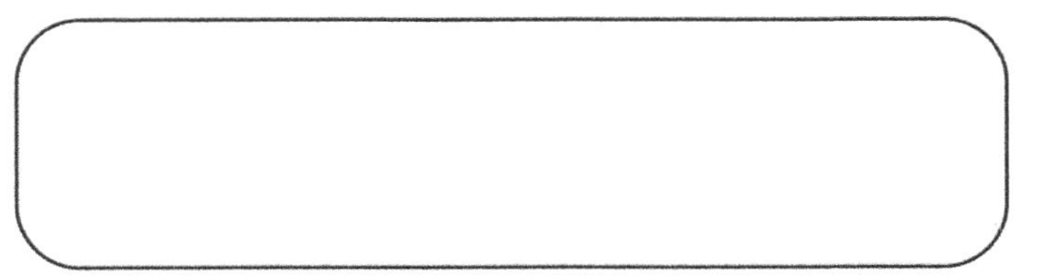

Answer

24. Rob has 7 straws in each bundle. How many straws does he have in 5 bundles?

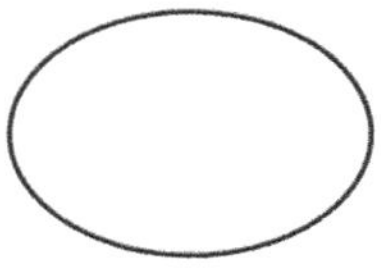

Answer

WORD PROBLEMS
MULTIPLICATION 9 TO 12

Name: ______________________

Date: __________ Time: __________

25. Emily recycles 11 cans each week. How many cans does she recycle in 9 weeks?

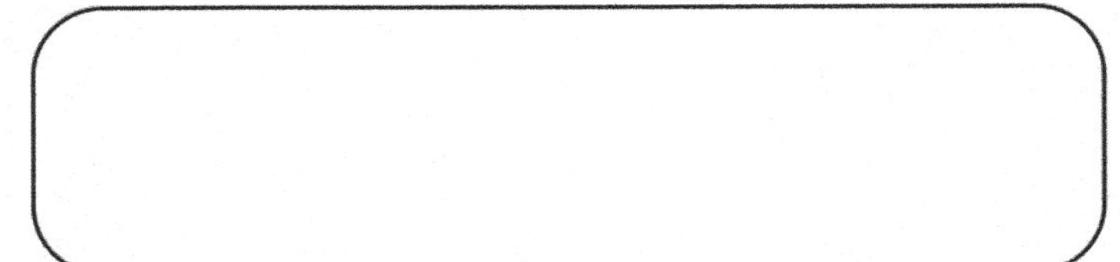

Answer

ACTIVITY CORNER

FIND A WAY

HELLO EVERYONE!

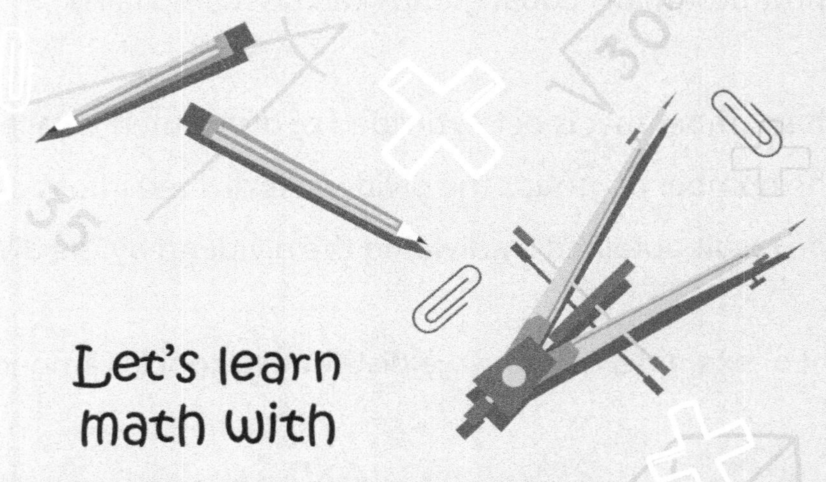

Let's learn math with

DIVISION

Shall we start?
Let's go!

DIVISION

Division is a method of distributing a group of things into **equal** parts. It is one of the four basic arithmetic operations that gives a fair result of sharing.
Division is the **inverse** operation of multiplication. The main goal of division is to know how many equal groups can be shared fairly.

The number that is being divided or distributed is called the **dividend**.
The number of groups the dividend is divided into is called the **divisor**.
The result obtained by dividing the dividend by the divisor is called the **quotient**.

For example, how can we distribute 6 cookies among 3 kids?

     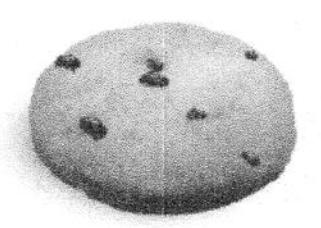

$6 \div 3 = 2$

Here, 6 is the **dividend**, 3 is the **divisor**, and 2 is the **quotient**.

This means that each child gets 2 cookies.

Note that, the dividend is always the largest number of the three in proper division sentences.

Unlike multiplication, the operands - dividend and divisor cannot be interchanged in a division operation.

Special facts about division:

- If the divisor is 1, then the quotient is equal to the dividend.
- As a corollary, if the dividend and divisor are equal, then the quotient is always 1.
- Division by zero is undefined.

DIVISION 0 TO 4

Name: ____________________

Date: __________ Time: __________

Score: /50

1. 2)68	2. 1)42	3. 1)68	4. 4)60	5. 1)30
6. 4)44	7. 1)27	8. 3)60	9. 2)62	10. 2)42
11. 1)76	12. 2)62	13. 3)99	14. 2)58	15. 1)67
16. 1)75	17. 1)47	18. 2)38	19. 2)4	20. 1)73
21. 1)36	22. 2)40	23. 2)4	24. 1)58	25. 3)18
26. 2)28	27. 3)84	28. 3)33	29. 3)78	30. 4)68
31. 2)42	32. 3)93	33. 1)24	34. 1)84	35. 2)72
36. 3)72	37. 1)23	38. 2)58	39. 3)24	40. 3)21
41. 3)72	42. 2)48	43. 4)24	44. 1)98	45. 2)10
46. 4)52	47. 3)18	48. 3)9	49. 1)87	50. 4)84

DIVISION 0 TO 4

Name: ____________________

Date: __________ Time: __________

1. $2\overline{)90}$	2. $3\overline{)54}$	3. $1\overline{)40}$	4. $2\overline{)96}$	5. $3\overline{)78}$
6. $3\overline{)27}$	7. $1\overline{)63}$	8. $3\overline{)42}$	9. $1\overline{)46}$	10. $4\overline{)72}$
11. $3\overline{)42}$	12. $1\overline{)8}$	13. $1\overline{)71}$	14. $4\overline{)68}$	15. $2\overline{)58}$
16. $3\overline{)33}$	17. $3\overline{)78}$	18. $3\overline{)15}$	19. $2\overline{)24}$	20. $4\overline{)80}$
21. $4\overline{)48}$	22. $3\overline{)42}$	23. $3\overline{)84}$	24. $3\overline{)75}$	25. $4\overline{)96}$
26. $4\overline{)16}$	27. $1\overline{)68}$	28. $4\overline{)36}$	29. $1\overline{)62}$	30. $1\overline{)42}$
31. $1\overline{)69}$	32. $1\overline{)82}$	33. $1\overline{)60}$	34. $2\overline{)86}$	35. $3\overline{)60}$
36. $1\overline{)77}$	37. $1\overline{)9}$	38. $1\overline{)94}$	39. $3\overline{)15}$	40. $3\overline{)12}$
41. $1\overline{)90}$	42. $3\overline{)69}$	43. $2\overline{)42}$	44. $2\overline{)52}$	45. $3\overline{)78}$
46. $1\overline{)71}$	47. $1\overline{)41}$	48. $1\overline{)73}$	49. $1\overline{)69}$	50. $4\overline{)80}$

DIVISION 0 TO 4

Name: ______________________

Date: __________ Time: __________

Score: /50

1. 1) 64	2. 1) 59	3. 4) 12	4. 1) 16	5. 2) 88
6. 1) 57	7. 1) 10	8. 1) 38	9. 1) 53	10. 1) 37
11. 4) 64	12. 1) 98	13. 3) 18	14. 3) 24	15. 3) 87
16. 2) 60	17. 4) 80	18. 2) 68	19. 1) 67	20. 4) 12
21. 2) 52	22. 3) 48	23. 1) 15	24. 1) 61	25. 2) 84
26. 3) 90	27. 3) 84	28. 1) 95	29. 3) 66	30. 1) 23
31. 3) 87	32. 2) 10	33. 2) 94	34. 2) 36	35. 4)
36. 2) 54	37. 2) 50	38. 3) 15	39. 2) 8	40. 3) 21
41. 1) 34	42. 1) 15	43. 1) 70	44. 3) 78	45. 1) 46
46. 2) 62	47. 2) 76	48. 2) 70	49. 1) 93	50. 2) 18

DIVISION 0 TO 4

Name: ____________ Date: ________ Time: ________

Score: /50

1. 1) 54	2. 3) 51	3. 3) 12	4. 1) 97	5. 1) 40
6. 4) 72	7. 2) 20	8. 2) 24	9. 1) 16	10. 3) 21
11. 2) 10	12. 1) 25	13. 1) 85	14. 3) 75	15. 2) 88
16. 4) 8	17. 1) 91	18. 1) 30	19. 1) 28	20. 3) 99
21. 1) 49	22. 4) 28	23. 2) 96	24. 3) 60	25. 1) 96
26. 1) 34	27. 3) 6	28. 3) 78	29. 1) 89	30. 2) 62
31. 1) 42	32. 1) 11	33. 3) 30	34. 1) 74	35. 1) 10
36. 1) 58	37. 4) 68	38. 3) 69	39. 1) 97	40. 2) 52
41. 4) 92	42. 1) 33	43. 3) 21	44. 1) 72	45. 1) 13
46. 1) 58	47. 1) 24	48. 2) 96	49. 2) 44	50. 2) 30

DIVISION 0 TO 4

Name: ____________________

Date: __________ Time: __________

Score: /50

1. $2\overline{)50}$	2. $1\overline{)23}$	3. $3\overline{)45}$	4. $1\overline{)93}$	5. $1\overline{)15}$
6. $1\overline{)7}$	7. $1\overline{)12}$	8. $1\overline{)33}$	9. $3\overline{)75}$	10. $1\overline{)15}$
11. $2\overline{)56}$	12. $2\overline{)78}$	13. $3\overline{)15}$	14. $3\overline{)36}$	15. $2\overline{)94}$
16. $3\overline{)87}$	17. $1\overline{)28}$	18. $3\overline{)63}$	19. $2\overline{)88}$	20. $3\overline{)75}$
21. $3\overline{)87}$	22. $1\overline{)17}$	23. $4\overline{)24}$	24. $1\overline{)70}$	25. $4\overline{)40}$
26. $4\overline{)4}$	27. $1\overline{)82}$	28. $4\overline{)60}$	29. $1\overline{)19}$	30. $3\overline{)93}$
31. $2\overline{)30}$	32. $3\overline{)42}$	33. $3\overline{)21}$	34. $1\overline{)27}$	35. $3\overline{)51}$
36. $4\overline{)44}$	37. $3\overline{)63}$	38. $4\overline{)20}$	39. $1\overline{)73}$	40. $1\overline{)47}$
41. $2\overline{)44}$	42. $4\overline{)72}$	43. $1\overline{)83}$	44. $1\overline{)10}$	45. $4\overline{)88}$
46. $2\overline{)16}$	47. $1\overline{)42}$	48. $1\overline{)20}$	49. $1\overline{)56}$	50. $1\overline{)61}$

DIVISION 0 TO 4

Name: ____________________

Date: __________ Time: __________

Score: /50

1. 2)16	2. 3)21	3. 3)15	4. 1)55	5. 2)72
6. 3)93	7. 2)48	8. 2)82	9. 3)93	10. 2)60
11. 1)21	12. 1)75	13. 3)	14. 2)80	15. 3)84
16. 3)33	17. 3)33	18. 1)21	19. 3)30	20. 1)52
21. 2)28	22. 2)82	23. 1)39	24. 2)78	25. 1)43
26. 3)12	27. 3)6	28. 1)15	29. 1)29	30. 2)26
31. 2)70	32. 4)20	33. 4)64	34. 3)60	35. 4)24
36. 2)50	37. 1)92	38. 4)20	39. 2)18	40. 1)50
41. 1)90	42. 2)16	43. 1)78	44. 1)37	45. 3)90
46. 4)16	47. 2)18	48. 1)57	49. 3)57	50. 1)7

DIVISION 0 TO 4

Name: ____________________

Date: __________ Time: __________

Score: /50

1. $3 \overline{)57}$	2. $2 \overline{)44}$	3. $3 \overline{)66}$	4. $4 \overline{)12}$	5. $2 \overline{)48}$
6. $1 \overline{)61}$	7. $4 \overline{)44}$	8. $1 \overline{)52}$	9. $4 \overline{)40}$	10. $4 \overline{)84}$
11. $4 \overline{)68}$	12. $3 \overline{)39}$	13. $1 \overline{)13}$	14. $2 \overline{)82}$	15. $1 \overline{)44}$
16. $3 \overline{)18}$	17. $2 \overline{)84}$	18. $3 \overline{)45}$	19. $3 \overline{)72}$	20. $3 \overline{)24}$
21. $3 \overline{)12}$	22. $1 \overline{)32}$	23. $1 \overline{)44}$	24. $1 \overline{)96}$	25. $3 \overline{)27}$
26. $2 \overline{)20}$	27. $2 \overline{)36}$	28. $1 \overline{)93}$	29. $3 \overline{)90}$	30. $3 \overline{)39}$
31. $2 \overline{)64}$	32. $1 \overline{)61}$	33. $3 \overline{)48}$	34. $3 \overline{)72}$	35. $2 \overline{)22}$
36. $2 \overline{)84}$	37. $3 \overline{)78}$	38. $2 \overline{)24}$	39. $1 \overline{)18}$	40. $1 \overline{)28}$
41. $1 \overline{)95}$	42. $2 \overline{)98}$	43. $1 \overline{)7}$	44. $1 \overline{)88}$	45. $2 \overline{)56}$
46. $1 \overline{)72}$	47. $2 \overline{)20}$	48. $3 \overline{)99}$	49. $2 \overline{)54}$	50. $3 \overline{)72}$

DIVISION 0 TO 4

Name: ______________________

Date: __________ Time: __________

Score: /50

1. $2\overline{)54}$	2. $3\overline{)87}$	3. $1\overline{)36}$	4. $1\overline{)66}$	5. $2\overline{)40}$
6. $2\overline{)78}$	7. $1\overline{)19}$	8. $3\overline{)93}$	9. $3\overline{)69}$	10. $3\overline{)99}$
11. $2\overline{)58}$	12. $2\overline{)}$	13. $1\overline{)55}$	14. $3\overline{)54}$	15. $1\overline{)25}$
16. $3\overline{)54}$	17. $2\overline{)40}$	18. $2\overline{)78}$	19. $3\overline{)}$	20. $4\overline{)12}$
21. $3\overline{)87}$	22. $2\overline{)16}$	23. $3\overline{)81}$	24. $1\overline{)66}$	25. $1\overline{)17}$
26. $1\overline{)57}$	27. $4\overline{)60}$	28. $1\overline{)31}$	29. $2\overline{)84}$	30. $4\overline{)88}$
31. $3\overline{)63}$	32. $2\overline{)74}$	33. $4\overline{)84}$	34. $3\overline{)69}$	35. $1\overline{)79}$
36. $1\overline{)19}$	37. $3\overline{)}$	38. $1\overline{)15}$	39. $3\overline{)81}$	40. $3\overline{)57}$
41. $2\overline{)30}$	42. $1\overline{)89}$	43. $1\overline{)84}$	44. $2\overline{)92}$	45. $2\overline{)76}$
46. $2\overline{)12}$	47. $1\overline{)77}$	48. $1\overline{)97}$	49. $1\overline{)86}$	50. $1\overline{)19}$

DIVIDE THE NUMBERS

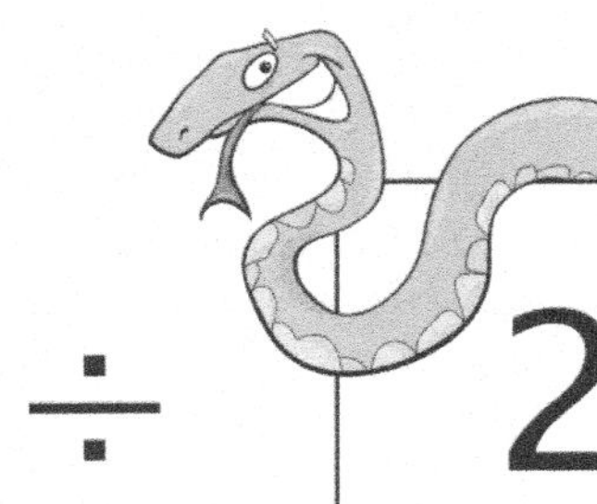

10	÷	2	=	

6	÷	3	=	

5	÷	1	=	

WORD PROBLEMS
DIVISION 0 TO 4

Name: ____________________

Date: __________ Time: __________

1. James had 20 short stories. If he wrote 2 short stories in each notebook, how many notebooks were there?

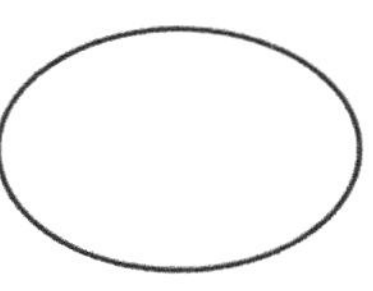

ANSWER

2. Dan had 24 lilies. If he planted 4 lilies in each planter box, how many planter boxes were there?

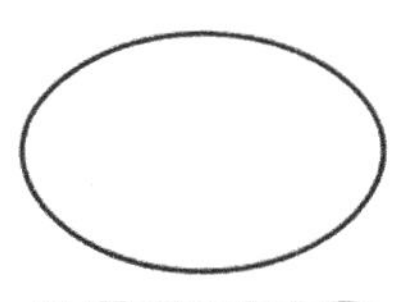

ANSWER

3. Eli had 15 pine cones. If he placed 3 pine cones in each pile, how many piles were there?

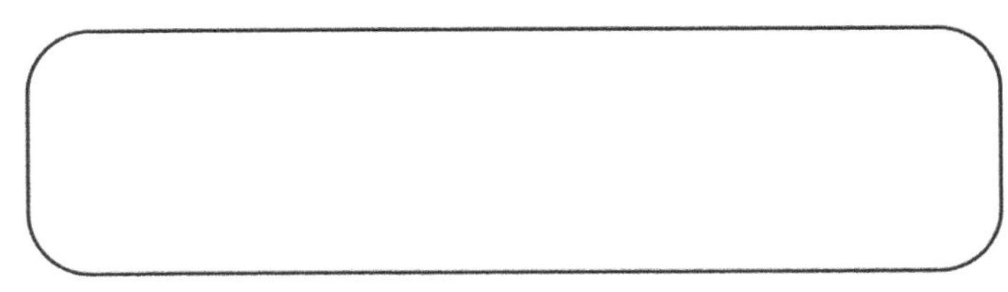
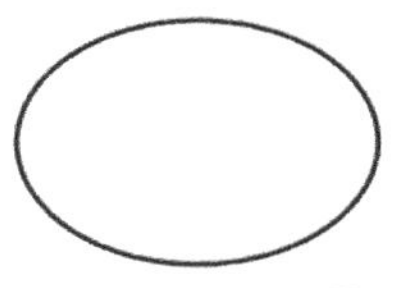

ANSWER

4. Each tank at the pet store has 3 tadpoles. If there are 30 tadpoles all together, how many tanks are there?

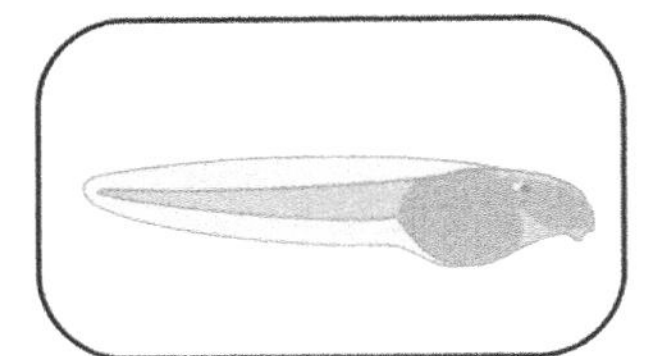

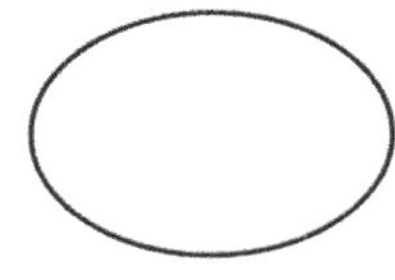

ANSWER

WORD PROBLEMS
DIVISION 0 TO 4

Name: ____________________
Date: __________ Time: __________

5. Each pile of laundry has 4 shirts. If there are 20 shirts all together, how many piles are there?

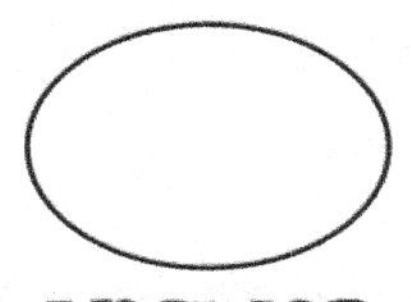

ANSWER

6. Each basket in the grocery store has 4 potatoes. If there are 40 potatoes all together, how many baskets are there?

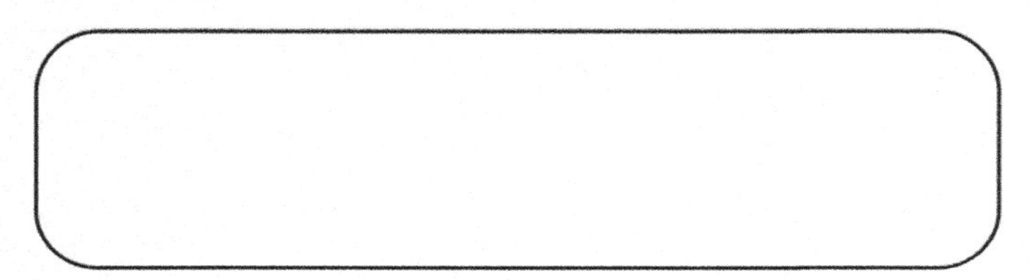
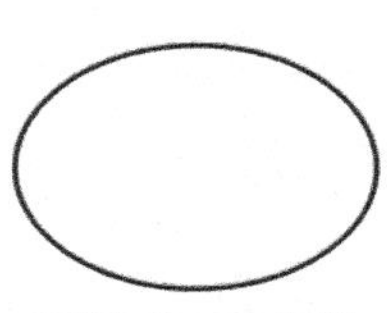

ANSWER

7. Piper had 24 poems. If she wrote 3 poems in each notebook, how many notebooks were there?

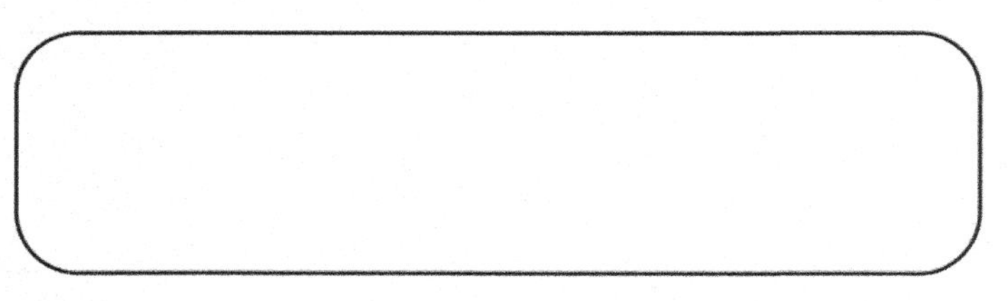

ANSWER

8. Each table in the cafeteria has 2 third graders. If there are 18 third graders all together, how many tables are there?

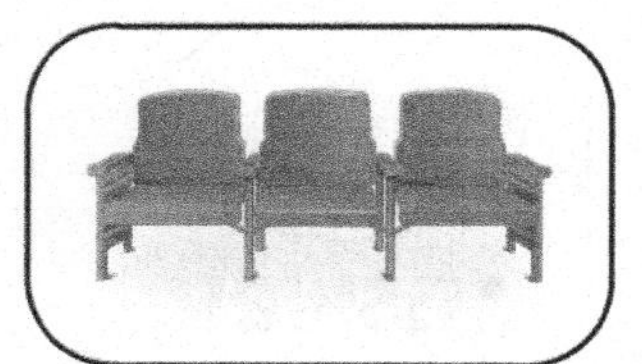

ANSWER

WORD PROBLEMS
DIVISION 0 TO 4

Name: ______________________

Date: __________ Time: __________

9. Josie had 14 napkins. If she placed 2 napkins in each stack, how many stacks were there?

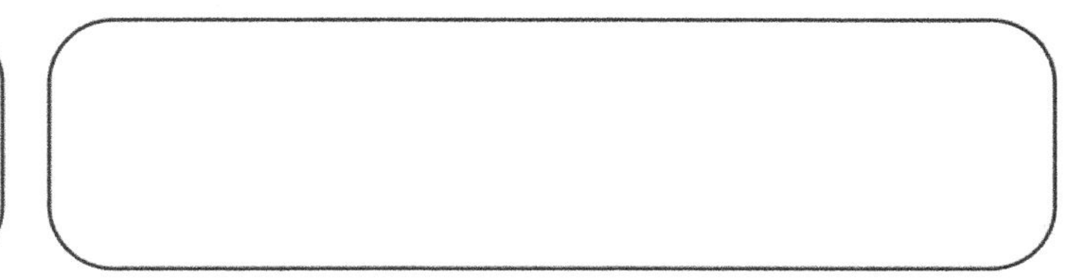

Answer

10. Paige had 10 t-shirts. If she placed 2 t-shirts in each stack, how many stacks were there?

Answer

11. Amanda bakes four brownies to share it equally with her friend Nancy. How many brownies does each one get?

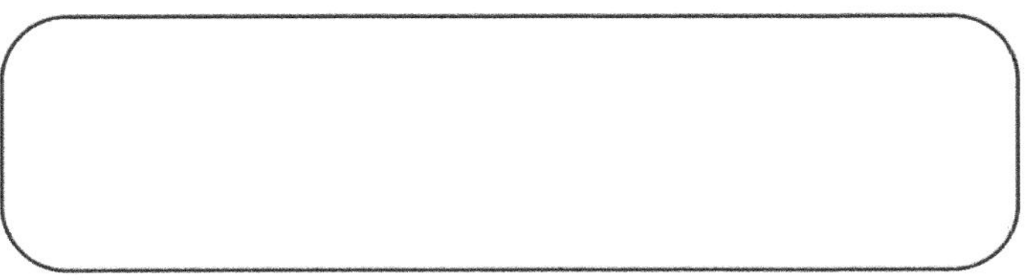
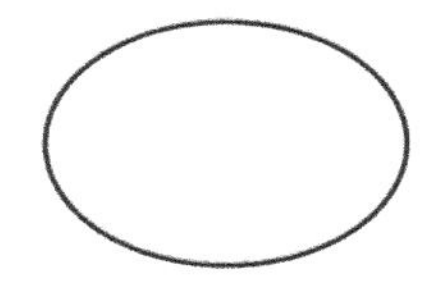

Answer

12. Mark and Tom run 8 miles in a relay race. How far should each run to cover an equal distance?

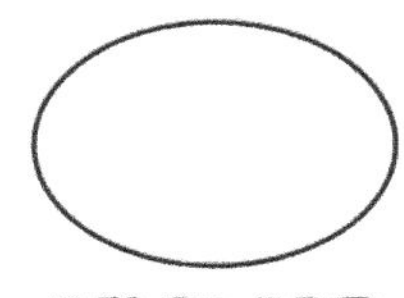

Answer

DIVIDE THE NUMBERS

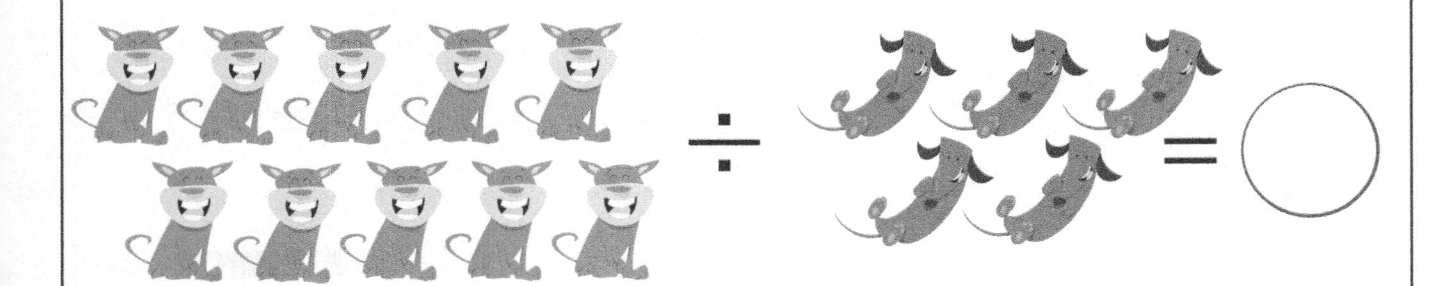

÷ =

÷

=

WORD PROBLEMS

DIVISION 0 TO 4

Name: ____________________

Date: __________ Time: __________

13. Susan has to read 30 pages of a book. She divides them equally to read it for three days. How many pages does she read in a day?

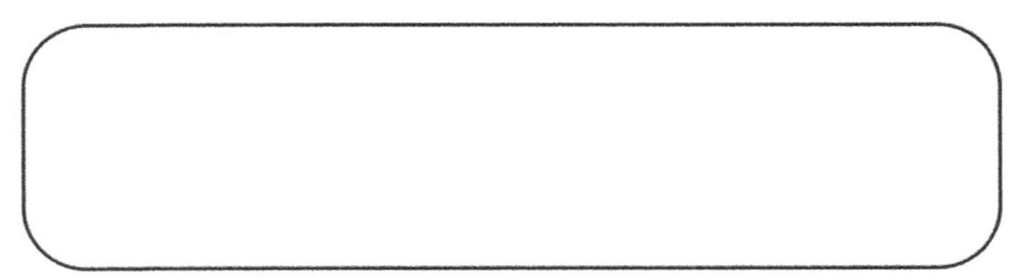

Answer

14. Mr. Derek has 28 postcards. He puts them into 4 equal piles. How many postcards are in each pile?

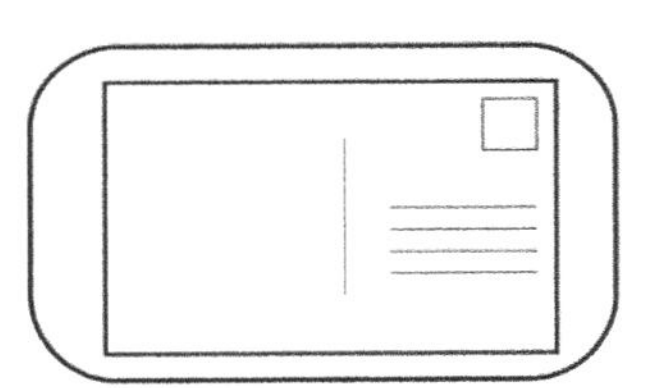

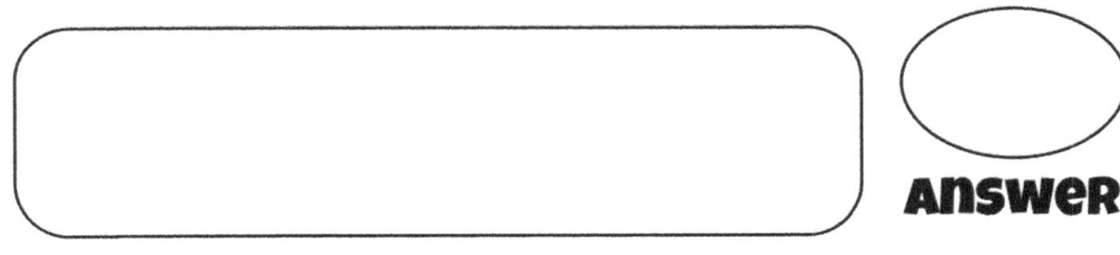

Answer

15. Lima bought 27 boxes of orange and distributed it between her two friends. How many oranges would each of her friends get?

Answer

16. In a school group of 15 students are seated equally in 3 rows. How many students will be seated in each row and how many would be left without a seat?

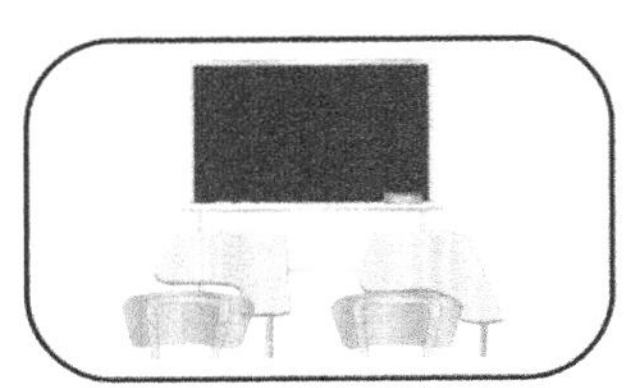

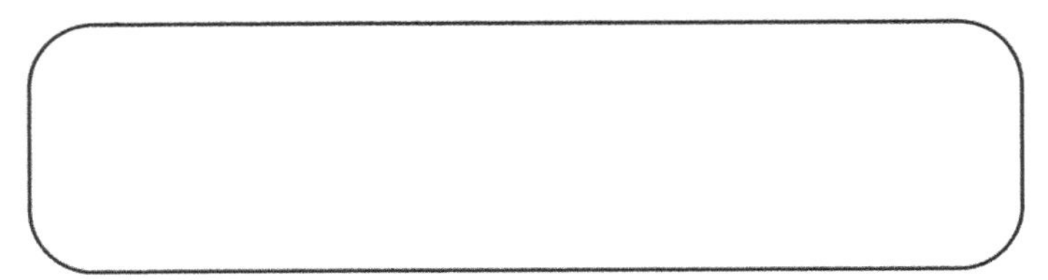

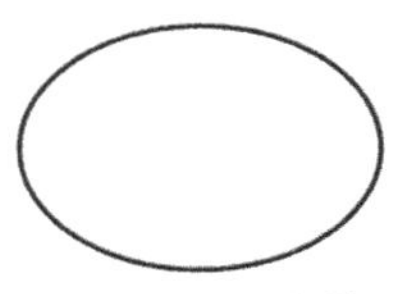

Answer

WORD PROBLEMS
DIVISION 0 TO 4

Name: ____________________

Date: __________ Time: __________

17. Sarah harvested 28 strawberries and packed them equally in four different boxes. How many strawberries would be packed in each box?

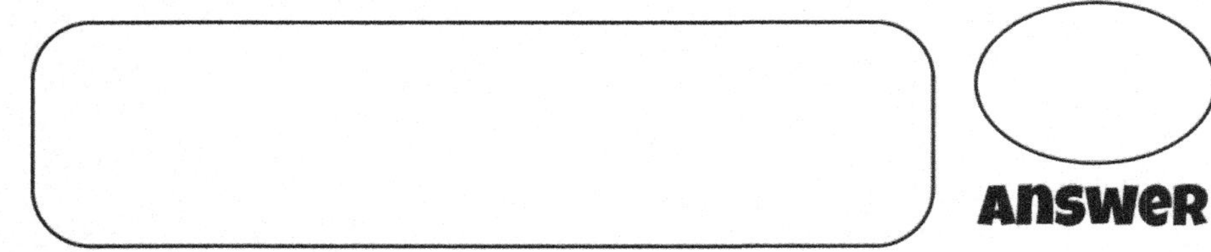

ANSWER

18. Luke and Mill collect 16 candies during the Trick or Treat hunt. They decide to divide the candies equally. How many candies would each get?

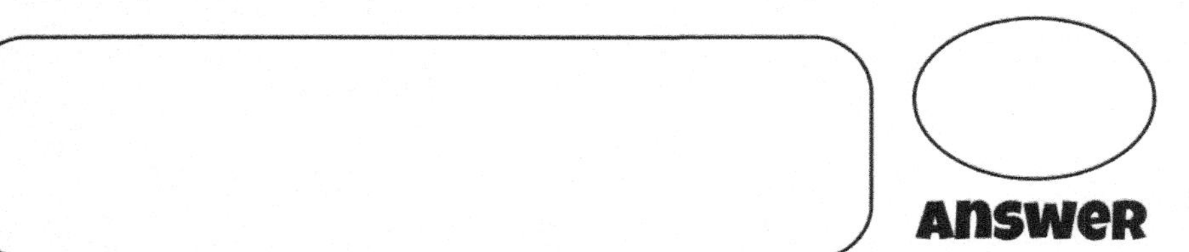

ANSWER

19. Ria had 20 badges. She divides them equally with her 4 friends. How many badges did each of them get?

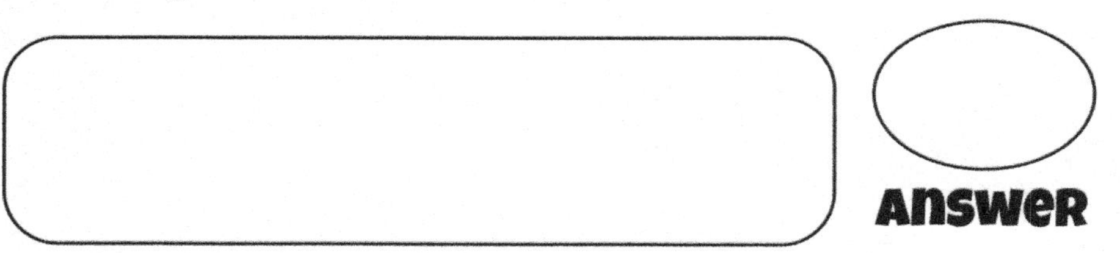

ANSWER

20. Jerry packs 36 cupcakes in 4 packs. How many cupcakes will be there in each pack?

ANSWER

WORD PROBLEMS
DIVISION 0 TO 4

Name: ____________________

Date: __________ Time: __________

21. Sheerin has 9 cookies. She packs equally into 3 boxes. How many cookies will be there in each box?

Answer

22. There are 32 flags. If you divide them into 4 groups, how many flags will be there in each group?

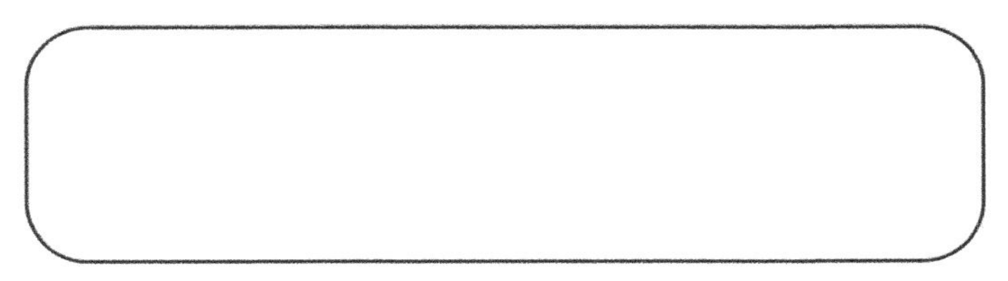

Answer

23. If 4 is divided by 0. What will be the quotient?

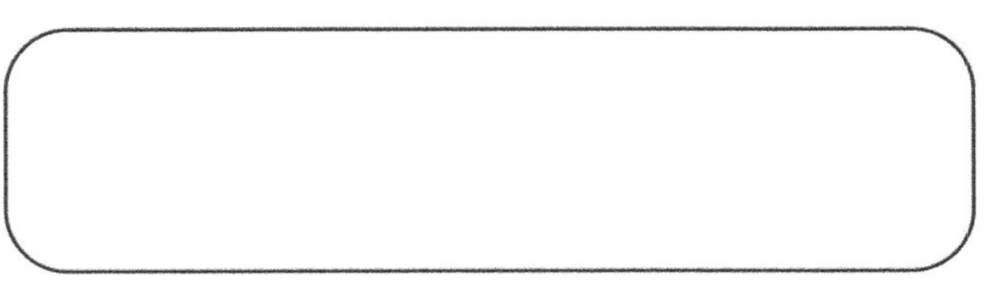
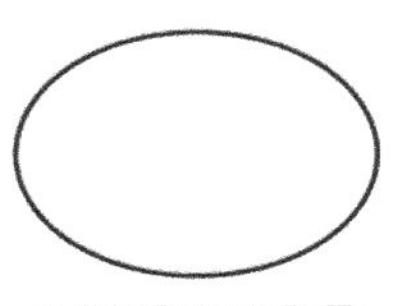

Answer

24. If 3 is divided by 0. What will be the quotient?

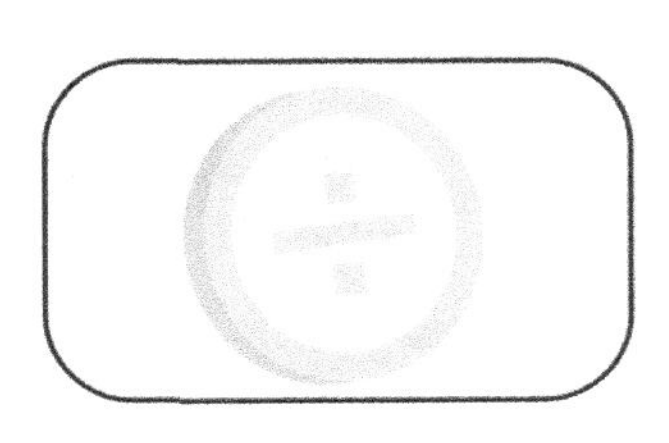

Answer

WORD PROBLEMS
DIVISION 0 TO 4

Name: ____________________
Date: __________ Time: __________

25. If 2 is divided by 1. What will be the quotient?

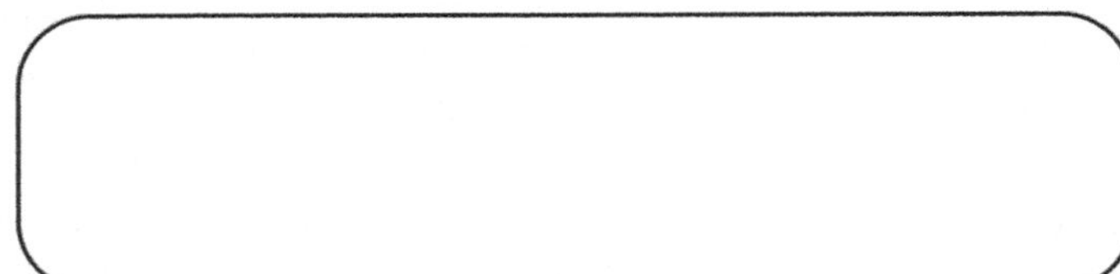

ANSWER

ACTIVITY CORNER

COLORING ACTIVITY

DIVISION 5 TO 8

Name: ____________________

Date: __________ Time: __________

Score: /50

1. $8\overline{)24}$	2. $6\overline{)12}$	3. $6\overline{)114}$	4. $7\overline{)70}$	5. $6\overline{)90}$
6. $6\overline{)60}$	7. $7\overline{)28}$	8. $7\overline{)28}$	9. $8\overline{)16}$	10. $7\overline{)63}$
11. $6\overline{)18}$	12. $8\overline{)96}$	13. $8\overline{)8}$	14. $5\overline{)95}$	15. $6\overline{)72}$
16. $6\overline{)12}$	17. $6\overline{)108}$	18. $8\overline{)40}$	19. $8\overline{)72}$	20. $6\overline{)72}$
21. $8\overline{)80}$	22. $6\overline{)18}$	23. $7\overline{)21}$	24. $8\overline{)40}$	25. $6\overline{)84}$
26. $5\overline{)15}$	27. $7\overline{)112}$	28. $7\overline{)119}$	29. $6\overline{)24}$	30. $6\overline{)102}$
31. $6\overline{)72}$	32. $6\overline{)30}$	33. $6\overline{)72}$	34. $8\overline{)16}$	35. $7\overline{)42}$
36. $6\overline{)6}$	37. $7\overline{)56}$	38. $8\overline{)0}$	39. $5\overline{)40}$	40. $6\overline{)78}$
41. $6\overline{)54}$	42. $6\overline{)24}$	43. $8\overline{)80}$	44. $7\overline{)77}$	45. $7\overline{)63}$
46. $5\overline{)90}$	47. $6\overline{)114}$	48. $6\overline{)6}$	49. $8\overline{)72}$	50. $8\overline{)112}$

DIVISION 5 TO 8

Name: ____________________

Date: __________ Time: __________

Score: /50

1. $7\overline{)77}$	2. $6\overline{)66}$	3. $8\overline{)56}$	4. $6\overline{)6}$	5. $5\overline{)95}$
6. $7\overline{)105}$	7. $7\overline{)14}$	8. $5\overline{)20}$	9. $6\overline{)84}$	10. $7\overline{)7}$
11. $8\overline{)64}$	12. $8\overline{)64}$	13. $6\overline{)78}$	14. $6\overline{)84}$	15. $7\overline{)91}$
16. $5\overline{)80}$	17. $6\overline{)12}$	18. $8\overline{)56}$	19. $5\overline{)85}$	20. $6\overline{)66}$
21. $6\overline{)54}$	22. $6\overline{)30}$	23. $7\overline{)63}$	24. $7\overline{)42}$	25. $5\overline{)115}$
26. $6\overline{)102}$	27. $6\overline{)12}$	28. $6\overline{)48}$	29. $5\overline{)20}$	30. $7\overline{)35}$
31. $7\overline{)77}$	32. $5\overline{)45}$	33. $8\overline{)80}$	34. $7\overline{)35}$	35. $8\overline{)80}$
36. $8\overline{)104}$	37. $7\overline{)70}$	38. $7\overline{)112}$	39. $8\overline{)88}$	40. $7\overline{)91}$
41. $6\overline{)24}$	42. $7\overline{)70}$	43. $6\overline{)30}$	44. $7\overline{)98}$	45. $8\overline{)24}$
46. $6\overline{)42}$	47. $7\overline{)91}$	48. $8\overline{)96}$	49. $7\overline{)49}$	50. $6\overline{)60}$

DIVISION 5 TO 8

Name: ____________________

Date: __________ Time: __________

Score: /50

1. 6) 90	2. 7) 70	3. 7) 49	4. 6) 108	5. 7) 105
6. 7) 7	7. 6) 90	8. 7) 77	9. 6) 60	10. 8) 80
11. 8) 80	12. 8) 104	13. 5) 75	14. 7) 112	15. 7) 70
16. 6) 114	17. 8) 64	18. 7) 98	19. 7) 7	20. 6) 6
21. 8) 0	22. 8) 64	23. 6) 102	24. 7) 70	25. 6) 42
26. 5) 50	27. 6) 12	28. 6) 90	29. 6) 12	30. 5) 30
31. 5) 105	32. 6) 114	33. 8) 40	34. 7) 119	35. 5) 50
36. 8) 24	37. 6) 78	38. 6) 78	39. 6) 78	40. 5) 105
41. 7) 28	42. 6) 114	43. 6) 66	44. 6) 12	45. 7) 77
46. 6) 84	47. 6) 36	48. 7) 49	49. 8) 16	50. 7) 56

DIVISION 5 TO 8

Name: ____________________

Date: __________ Time: __________

Score: /50

1. $7\overline{)70}$	2. $7\overline{)7}$	3. $7\overline{)91}$	4. $6\overline{)102}$	5. $7\overline{)35}$
6. $6\overline{)48}$	7. $6\overline{)60}$	8. $5\overline{)20}$	9. $7\overline{)91}$	10. $7\overline{)7}$
11. $8\overline{)16}$	12. $6\overline{)102}$	13. $8\overline{)88}$	14. $8\overline{)16}$	15. $7\overline{)21}$
16. $6\overline{)24}$	17. $5\overline{)25}$	18. $6\overline{)102}$	19. $8\overline{)96}$	20. $6\overline{)108}$
21. $8\overline{)96}$	22. $6\overline{)72}$	23. $7\overline{)84}$	24. $8\overline{)8}$	25. $6\overline{)66}$
26. $7\overline{)105}$	27. $7\overline{)112}$	28. $6\overline{)84}$	29. $5\overline{)15}$	30. $8\overline{)32}$
31. $6\overline{)24}$	32. $5\overline{)10}$	33. $5\overline{)60}$	34. $6\overline{)30}$	35. $7\overline{)70}$
36. $7\overline{)63}$	37. $8\overline{)104}$	38. $5\overline{)10}$	39. $5\overline{)60}$	40. $7\overline{)98}$
41. $6\overline{)18}$	42. $7\overline{)84}$	43. $6\overline{)48}$	44. $7\overline{)91}$	45. $8\overline{)96}$
46. $8\overline{)8}$	47. $7\overline{)35}$	48. $7\overline{)28}$	49. $8\overline{)104}$	50. $5\overline{)20}$

DIVISION 5 TO 8

Name: ____________________

Date: __________ Time: __________

Score: /50

1. 7)7	2. 6)60	3. 5)70	4. 7)56	5. 6)24
6. 6)96	7. 7)56	8. 6)30	9. 8)32	10. 6)108
11. 7)14	12. 7)7	13. 6)108	14. 6)108	15. 6)54
16. 7)105	17. 7)14	18. 6)72	19. 6)42	20. 6)6
21. 6)36	22. 7)70	23. 6)108	24. 8)64	25. 6)18
26. 7)21	27. 8)16	28. 8)56	29. 7)35	30. 5)20
31. 7)49	32. 5)105	33. 7)49	34. 7)49	35. 7)84
36. 8)104	37. 7)49	38. 7)91	39. 6)42	40. 6)60
41. 7)112	42. 6)90	43. 8)40	44. 8)96	45. 6)72
46. 6)18	47. 6)72	48. 6)6	49. 6)66	50. 6)102

DIVISION 5 TO 8

Name: ____________________

Date: __________ Time: __________

Score: /50

1. 6) 36	2. 7) 63	3. 5) 105	4. 6) 114	5. 7) 7
6. 7) 42	7. 6) 78	8. 7) 28	9. 6) 114	10. 6) 102
11. 7) 14	12. 7) 63	13. 6)	14. 5) 20	15. 5) 35
16. 7) 91	17. 5) 105	18. 7) 98	19. 7) 56	20. 8) 64
21. 8) 24	22. 6) 42	23. 5) 105	24. 6) 54	25. 6) 84
26. 6) 60	27. 6) 108	28. 6) 24	29. 8) 32	30. 6) 96
31. 5) 65	32. 8) 56	33. 6) 30	34. 7) 77	35. 7) 21
36. 7) 112	37. 7) 7	38. 7) 49	39. 7) 56	40. 7) 21
41. 6) 36	42. 6) 54	43. 7) 49	44. 7) 56	45. 7) 105
46. 5) 100	47. 6) 114	48. 6) 36	49. 5) 40	50. 6) 42

DIVISION 5 TO 8

Name: ____________________

Date: __________ Time: __________

Score: /50

1. $6\overline{)96}$	2. $6\overline{)36}$	3. $7\overline{)63}$	4. $6\overline{)90}$	5. $6\overline{)96}$
6. $8\overline{)112}$	7. $7\overline{)105}$	8. $8\overline{)80}$	9. $7\overline{)91}$	10. $6\overline{)12}$
11. $6\overline{)78}$	12. $6\overline{)108}$	13. $7\overline{)42}$	14. $6\overline{)}$	15. $5\overline{)35}$
16. $5\overline{)75}$	17. $8\overline{)72}$	18. $6\overline{)66}$	19. $8\overline{)24}$	20. $6\overline{)108}$
21. $7\overline{)112}$	22. $6\overline{)54}$	23. $6\overline{)90}$	24. $8\overline{)80}$	25. $5\overline{)70}$
26. $6\overline{)96}$	27. $7\overline{)42}$	28. $6\overline{)102}$	29. $8\overline{)48}$	30. $7\overline{)112}$
31. $7\overline{)112}$	32. $6\overline{)48}$	33. $5\overline{)60}$	34. $6\overline{)78}$	35. $7\overline{)105}$
36. $6\overline{)30}$	37. $8\overline{)96}$	38. $7\overline{)63}$	39. $5\overline{)25}$	40. $5\overline{)10}$
41. $7\overline{)63}$	42. $7\overline{)105}$	43. $5\overline{)80}$	44. $8\overline{)40}$	45. $7\overline{)21}$
46. $6\overline{)96}$	47. $7\overline{)42}$	48. $7\overline{)49}$	49. $6\overline{)36}$	50. $8\overline{)104}$

DIVISION 5 TO 8

Name: ____________________

Date: __________ Time: __________

Score: /50

1. $8\overline{)80}$	2. $8\overline{)112}$	3. $5\overline{)30}$	4. $8\overline{)96}$	5. $8\overline{)56}$
6. $7\overline{)63}$	7. $5\overline{)70}$	8. $6\overline{)90}$	9. $5\overline{)5}$	10. $8\overline{)104}$
11. $6\overline{)84}$	12. $7\overline{)105}$	13. $7\overline{)112}$	14. $6\overline{)102}$	15. $7\overline{)28}$
16. $6\overline{)66}$	17. $5\overline{)90}$	18. $6\overline{)54}$	19. $8\overline{)80}$	20. $7\overline{)42}$
21. $7\overline{)56}$	22. $7\overline{)7}$	23. $7\overline{)98}$	24. $6\overline{)18}$	25. $6\overline{)12}$
26. $7\overline{)70}$	27. $7\overline{)7}$	28. $6\overline{)24}$	29. $5\overline{)90}$	30. $5\overline{)25}$
31. $7\overline{)98}$	32. $5\overline{)65}$	33. $6\overline{)54}$	34. $5\overline{)60}$	35. $6\overline{)54}$
36. $8\overline{)8}$	37. $5\overline{)55}$	38. $6\overline{)12}$	39. $5\overline{)70}$	40. $7\overline{)21}$
41. $7\overline{)112}$	42. $7\overline{)21}$	43. $6\overline{)36}$	44. $8\overline{)8}$	45. $6\overline{)72}$
46. $5\overline{)55}$	47. $8\overline{)56}$	48. $7\overline{)112}$	49. $6\overline{)96}$	50. $6\overline{)24}$

DIVIDE THE NUMBERS

$56 \div 8 =$

$81 \div 9 =$

$28 \div 7 =$

$12 \div 12 =$

WORD PROBLEMS
DIVISION 5 TO 8

Name: ______________________
Date: __________ Time: __________

1. Tessa, Leon, Jamie, and Ella donated an equal number of toys for charity. They donated a total of 32 toys. How many toys did each of them donate?

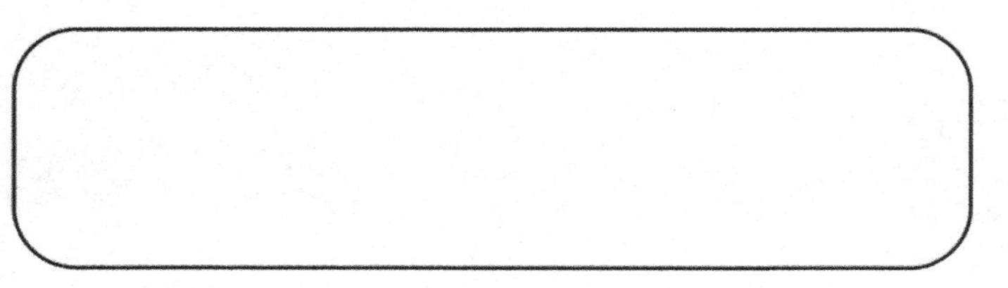

Answer

2. Manny has to hang pictures on 10 walls. He has 80 pictures altogether. How many pictures can he hang on each wall?

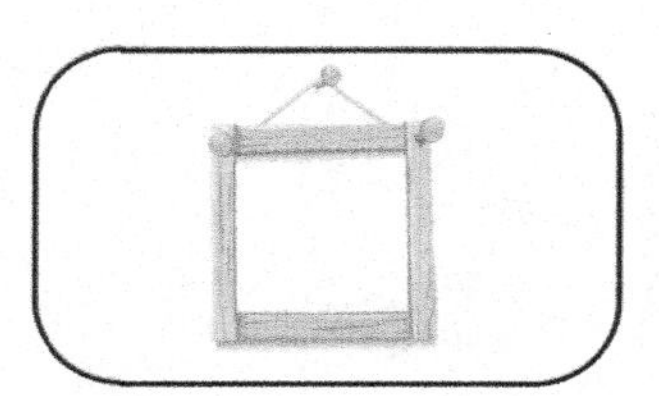

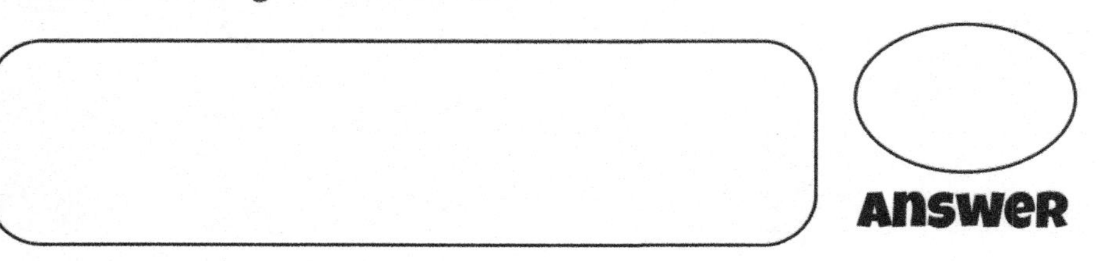

Answer

3. Bane has to divide 64 books into 8 piles with an equal number of books in each pile. How many books will each have?

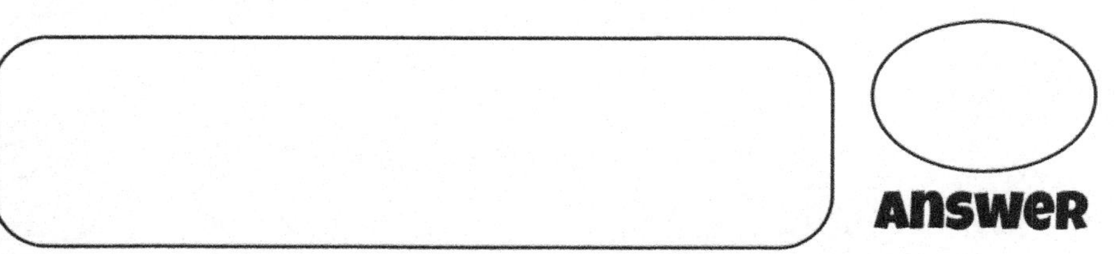

Answer

4. Adam has 63 cookies. He packs them equally in 7 boxes. How many cookies are there in each box?

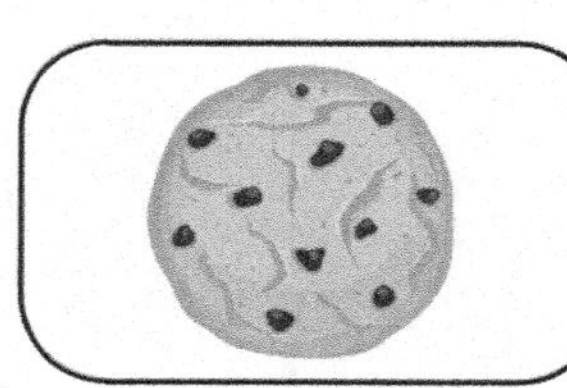

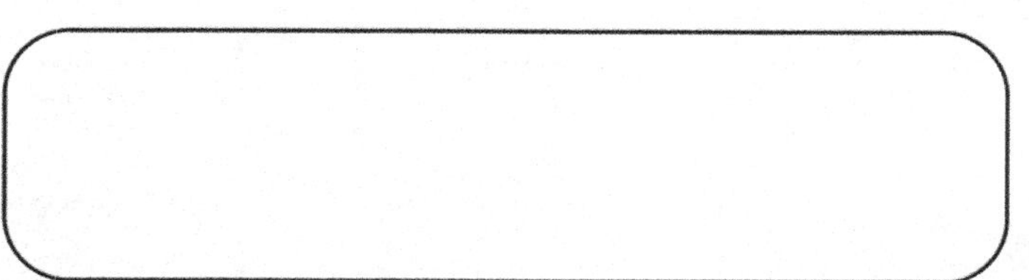

Answer

WORD PROBLEMS
DIVISION 5 TO 8

Name: ______________________

Date: __________ Time: __________

5. Harry has 72 treats. He shares them equally between his 8 dogs. How many treats does each dog get?

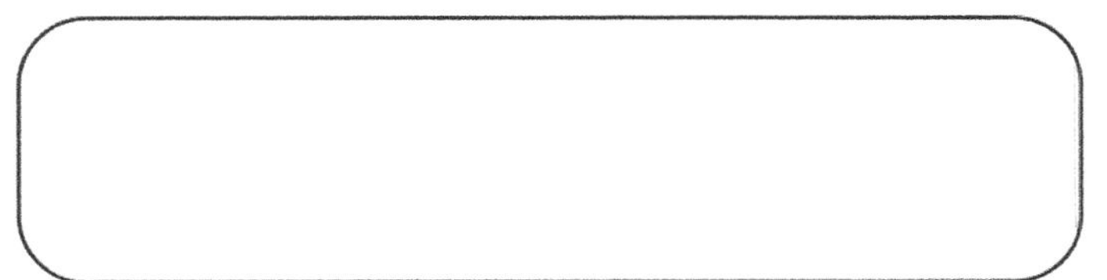

ANSWER

6. Danny, Ramona, Jess, and Amanda have 28 dice. They share the dominoes equally. How many dice does each have now?

ANSWER

7. Martha has 70 toffees. She gives 7 toffees to each of her friends. How man friends does Martha have

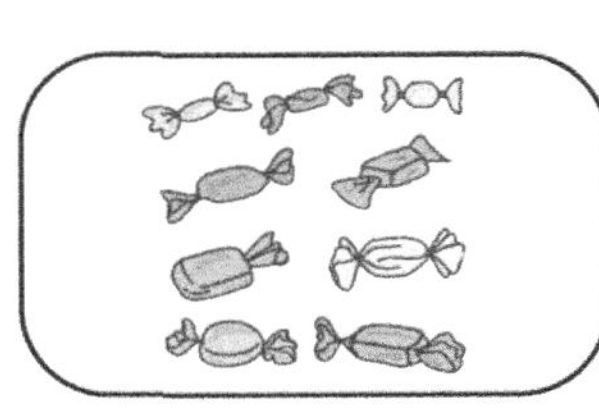

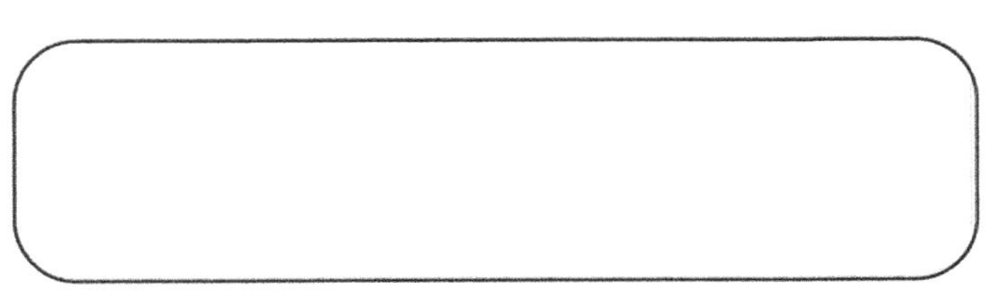

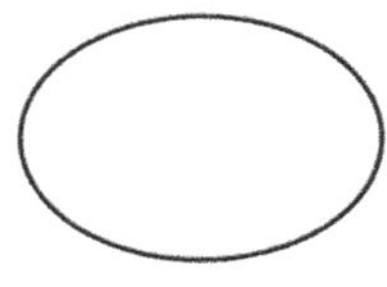

ANSWER

8. Eden has 72 flowers and 8 vases. How many flowers can she place in each vase to divide the flowers equally?

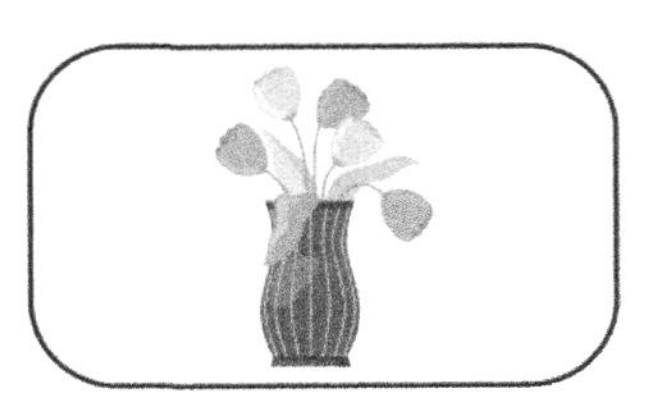

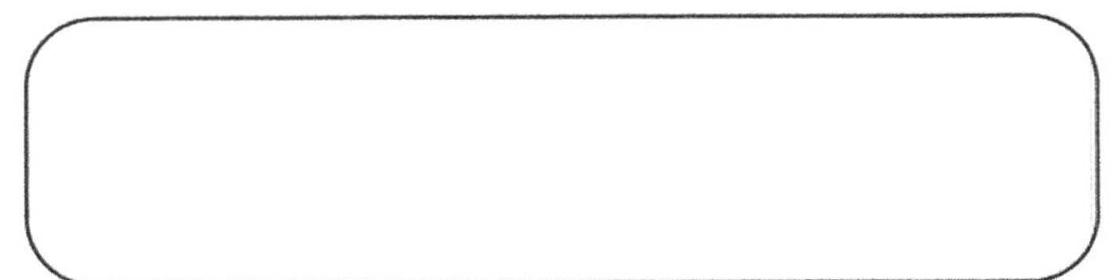

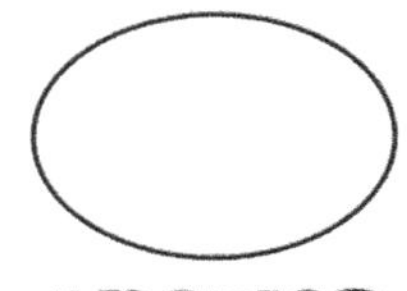

ANSWER

WORD PROBLEMS
DIVISION 5 TO 8

Name: ______________________
Date: __________ Time: __________

9. We have 30 apples to give away to 6 children. How many apples can be given to each child?

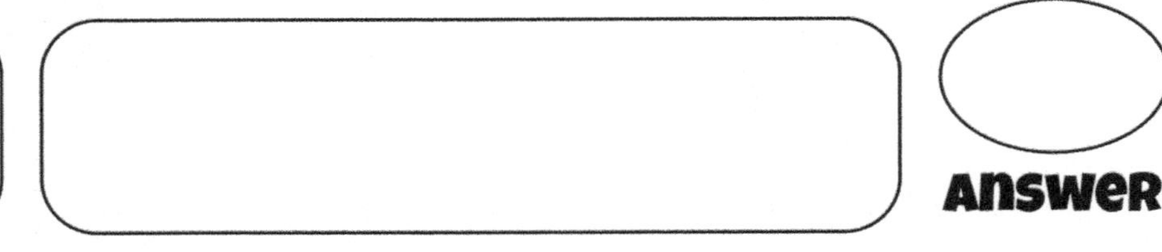

ANSWER

10. If 15 players are divided into teams of five, how many teams will be there?

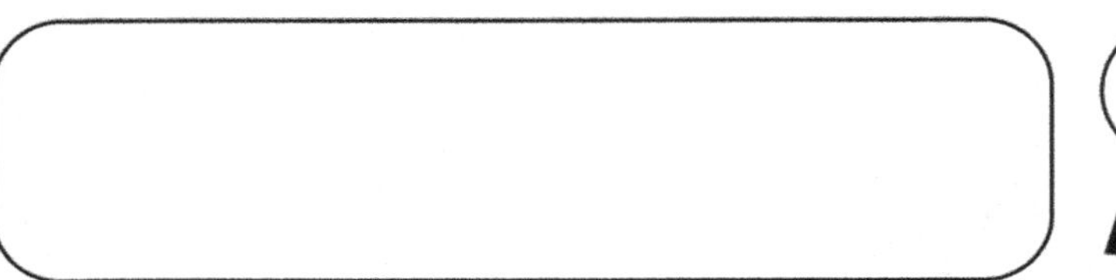

ANSWER

11. James collected 5 marbles. Lucas collected 35 marbles. Lucas collected how many times as many marbles as James?

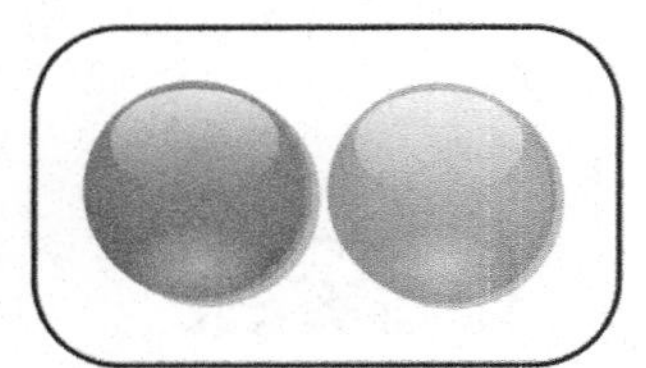
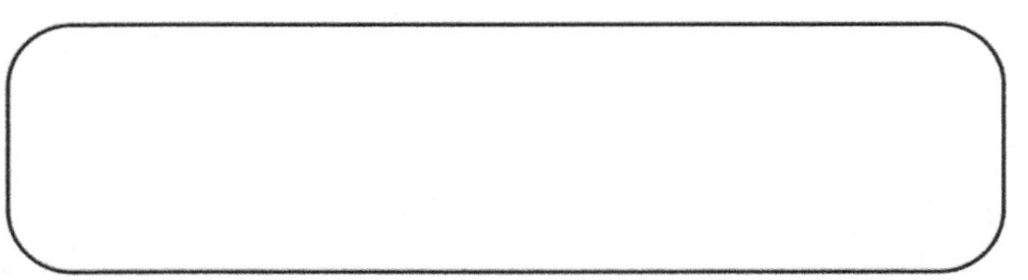

ANSWER

12. There are 56 newspapers on the shelf A and 7 newspapers on the shelf B. There are how many times as many newspapers on the shelf A as on the shelf B?

ANSWER

FIND THE 10 DIFFERENCES

WORD PROBLEMS
DIVISION 5 TO 8

Name: ______________________

Date: __________ Time: __________

13. Chance folded 6 towels. Liz folded 48 towels. Liz folded how many times as many towels as Chance?

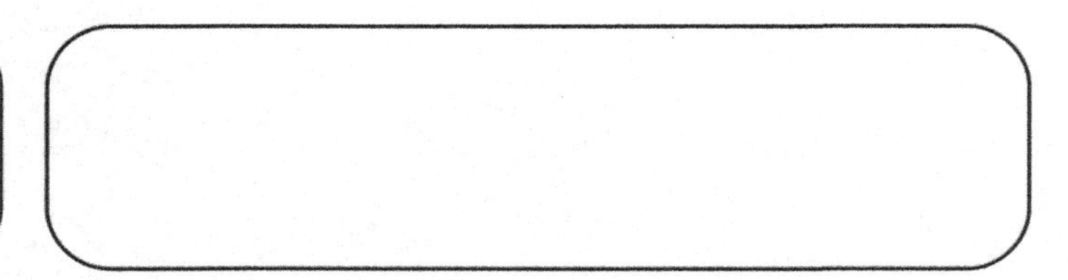

ANSWER

14. Sue baked 7 cupcakes. June baked 49 cupcakes. June baked how many times as many cupcakes as Sue?

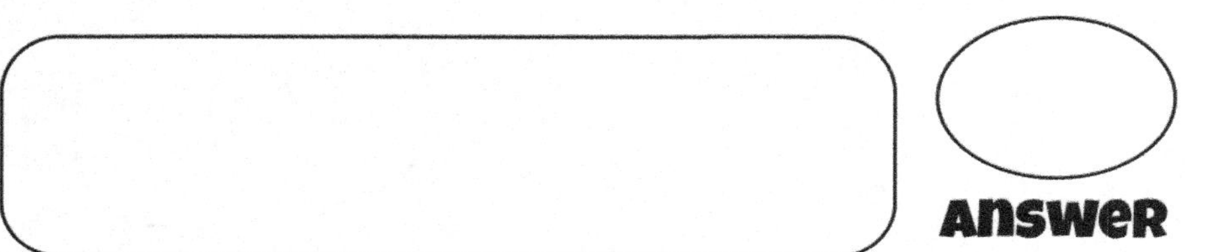

ANSWER

15. Grace wrote 6 paragraphs. Clark wrote 36 paragraphs. Clark wrote how many times as many paragraphs as Grace?

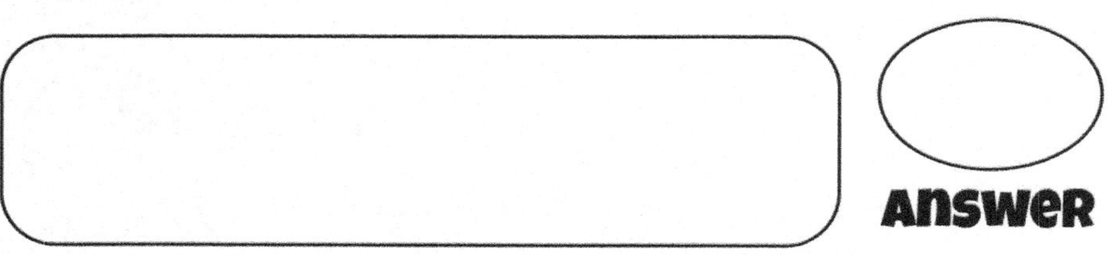

ANSWER

16. Gray drew 7 ants. Josie drew 70 ants. Josie drew how many times as many ants as Gray?

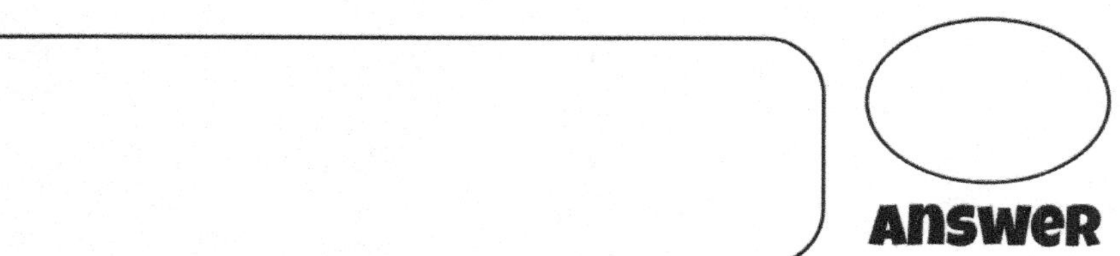

ANSWER

WORD PROBLEMS
DIVISION 5 TO 8

Name: ____________________

Date: __________ Time: __________

17. John gathered 8 pine cones. Ruth gathered 40 pine cones. Ruth gathered how many times as many pine cones as John?

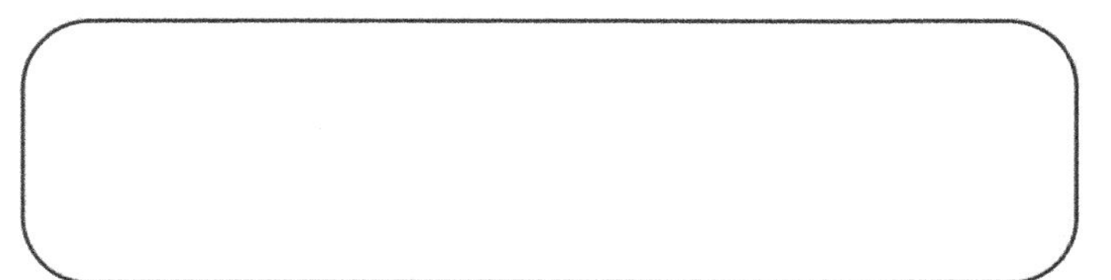
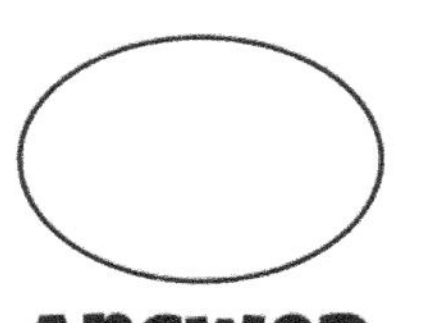

Answer

18. Gail picked up 63 seashells. Willow picked up 7 seashells. Willow picked up how many times as many seashells as Gail?

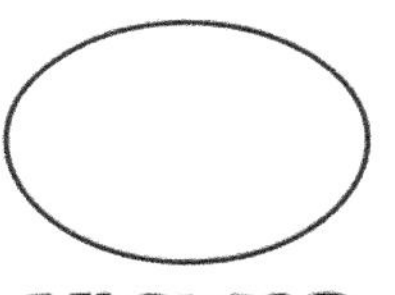

Answer

19. Greg wrote 3 essays. Jim wrote 27 essays. Jim wrote how many times as many essays as Greg?

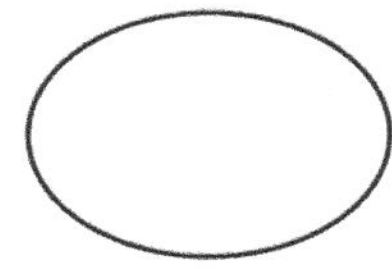

Answer

20. Sharpeners are packed in groups of 8. If there are 48 groups, how sharpeners are in each group?

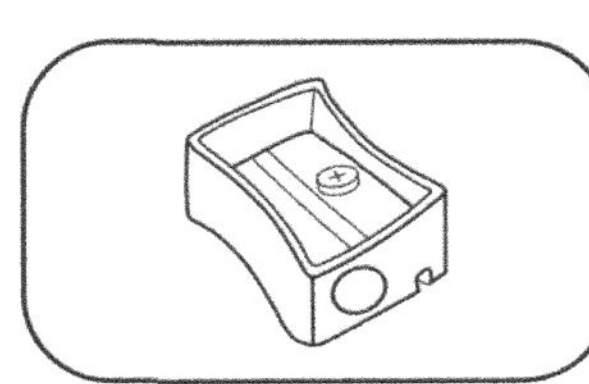

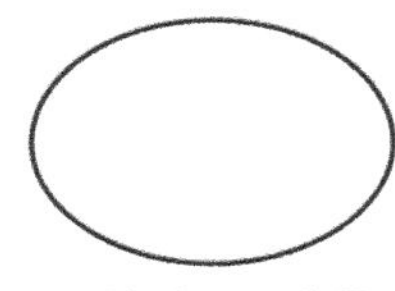

Answer

WORD PROBLEMS
DIVISION 5 TO 8

Name: ______________________

Date: __________ Time: __________

21. Laura took her 5 friends to a farm to pick apples. They picked 54 apples in all. How apples did each of them pick, each picked the same number of apples?

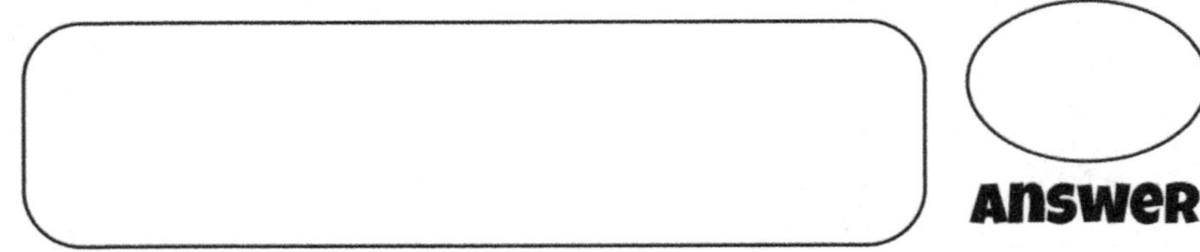

ANSWER

22. Sara collects 50 star stickers. If she pastes 5 stickers in each page, how many pages will she need to paste all the stickers?

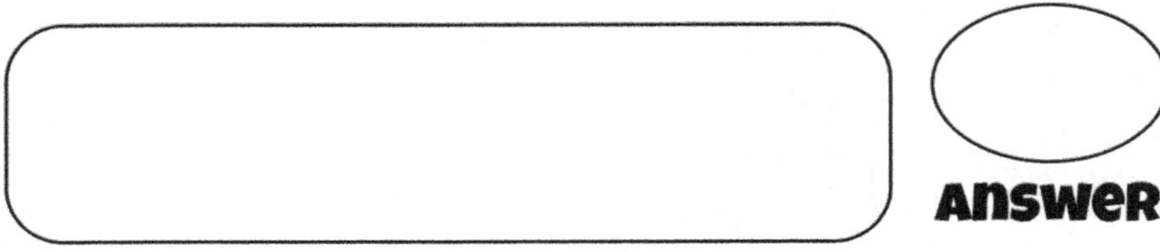

ANSWER

23. If 7 is divided by 7, what is the quotient?

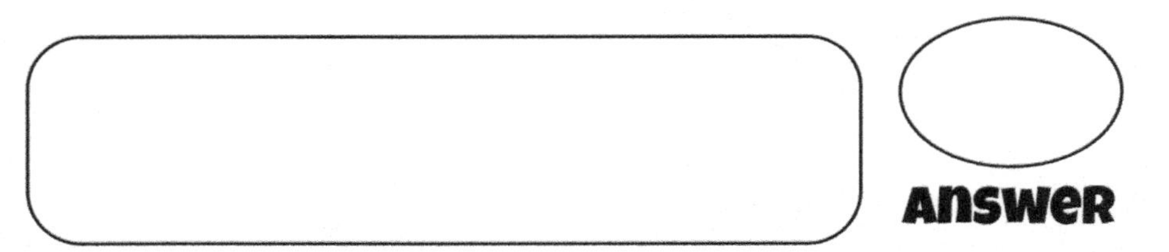

ANSWER

24. If 8 is divided by 1, what is the quotient?

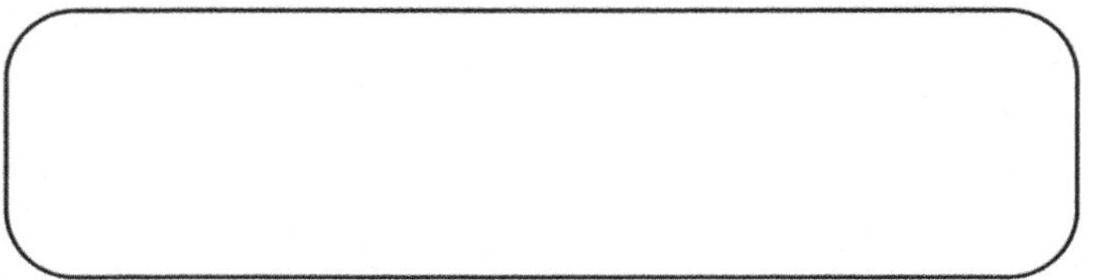

ANSWER

WORD PROBLEMS

DIVISION 5 TO 8

Name: ____________________

Date: __________ Time: __________

25. If 6 is divided by 6, what is the quotient?

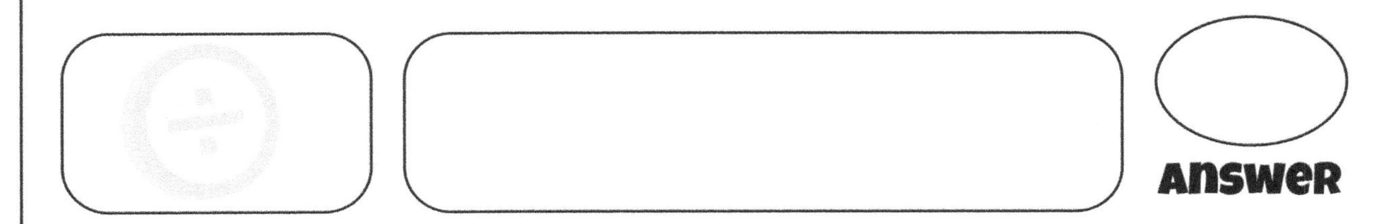

ANSWER

ACTIVITY CORNER

FIND A WAY

DIVISION 6 TO 12

Name: ____________
Date: ________ Time: ________

Score: /50

1. $9\overline{)81}$	2. $9\overline{)90}$	3. $11\overline{)33}$	4. $9\overline{)45}$	5. $10\overline{)90}$
6. $8\overline{)88}$	7. $8\overline{)88}$	8. $7\overline{)63}$	9. $11\overline{)88}$	10. $12\overline{)48}$
11. $9\overline{)54}$	12. $9\overline{)36}$	13. $10\overline{)30}$	14. $9\overline{)45}$	15. $7\overline{)49}$
16. $11\overline{)22}$	17. $9\overline{)18}$	18. $10\overline{)70}$	19. $7\overline{)84}$	20. $11\overline{)55}$
21. $6\overline{)54}$	22. $6\overline{)54}$	23. $11\overline{)88}$	24. $7\overline{)35}$	25. $11\overline{)66}$
26. $9\overline{)81}$	27. $7\overline{)28}$	28. $11\overline{)44}$	29. $8\overline{)40}$	30. $10\overline{)30}$
31. $10\overline{)40}$	32. $12\overline{)72}$	33. $8\overline{)88}$	34. $9\overline{)54}$	35. $11\overline{)77}$
36. $7\overline{)77}$	37. $9\overline{)63}$	38. $10\overline{)60}$	39. $11\overline{)77}$	40. $8\overline{)80}$
41. $6\overline{)96}$	42. $6\overline{)72}$	43. $7\overline{)63}$	44. $6\overline{)48}$	45. $12\overline{)96}$
46. $8\overline{)48}$	47. $11\overline{)66}$	48. $11\overline{)22}$	49. $7\overline{)77}$	50. $12\overline{)96}$

DIVISION 6 TO 12

Name: ____________________
Date: __________ Time: __________

Score: /50

1. 7) 84	2. 7) 49	3. 8) 56	4. 8) 40	5. 7) 35
6. 10) 60	7. 10) 70	8. 10) 80	9. 6) 66	10. 10) 70
11. 7) 77	12. 7) 28	13. 11) 33	14. 11) 55	15. 9) 81
16. 12) 36	17. 10) 50	18. 9) 18	19. 8) 40	20. 9) 63
21. 11) 88	22. 7) 91	23. 9) 63	24. 12) 60	25. 10) 70
26. 11) 33	27. 7) 49	28. 10) 80	29. 10) 70	30. 10) 80
31. 9) 72	32. 7) 42	33. 10) 70	34. 7) 35	35. 9) 45
36. 10) 50	37. 10) 30	38. 8) 24	39. 7) 49	40. 11) 33
41. 6) 60	42. 8) 48	43. 6) 30	44. 6) 96	45. 6) 72
46. 11) 55	47. 10) 50	48. 8) 72	49. 6) 24	50. 6) 72

DIVISION 6 TO 12

Name: ____________________
Date: __________ Time: __________

Score: /50

1. 6) 54	2. 8) 144	3. 8) 144	4. 9) 81	5. 9) 99
6. 6) 54	7. 10) 130	8. 12) 84	9. 10) 140	10. 11) 143
11. 12) 72	12. 9) 144	13. 7) 147	14. 12) 84	15. 6) 24
16. 10) 100	17. 10) 40	18. 8) 136	19. 10) 70	20. 7) 105
21. 6) 42	22. 9) 126	23. 9) 27	24. 10) 130	25. 7) 70
26. 11) 88	27. 11) 33	28. 10) 120	29. 9) 108	30. 7) 140
31. 11) 66	32. 12) 108	33. 7) 77	34. 9) 108	35. 7) 140
36. 8) 40	37. 10) 80	38. 11) 66	39. 12) 72	40. 7) 70
41. 8) 72	42. 6) 78	43. 10) 40	44. 10) 120	45. 8) 144
46. 10) 30	47. 12) 84	48. 10) 40	49. 12) 24	50. 7) 126

DIVISION 6 TO 12

Name: ____________________

Date: __________ Time: __________

Score: /50

1. $7\overline{)35}$	2. $11\overline{)66}$	3. $7\overline{)42}$	4. $6\overline{)48}$	5. $10\overline{)30}$
6. $9\overline{)81}$	7. $12\overline{)84}$	8. $8\overline{)112}$	9. $8\overline{)128}$	10. $9\overline{)126}$
11. $9\overline{)144}$	12. $10\overline{)60}$	13. $11\overline{)33}$	14. $6\overline{)54}$	15. $7\overline{)49}$
16. $10\overline{)140}$	17. $7\overline{)112}$	18. $10\overline{)130}$	19. $10\overline{)60}$	20. $10\overline{)20}$
21. $11\overline{)44}$	22. $9\overline{)72}$	23. $9\overline{)36}$	24. $9\overline{)126}$	25. $9\overline{)45}$
26. $10\overline{)130}$	27. $10\overline{)90}$	28. $9\overline{)99}$	29. $9\overline{)144}$	30. $7\overline{)42}$
31. $11\overline{)66}$	32. $11\overline{)33}$	33. $8\overline{)136}$	34. $8\overline{)144}$	35. $11\overline{)44}$
36. $12\overline{)72}$	37. $10\overline{)60}$	38. $10\overline{)120}$	39. $8\overline{)88}$	40. $9\overline{)81}$
41. $11\overline{)44}$	42. $9\overline{)36}$	43. $6\overline{)120}$	44. $9\overline{)54}$	45. $6\overline{)24}$
46. $8\overline{)56}$	47. $7\overline{)35}$	48. $6\overline{)144}$	49. $6\overline{)108}$	50. $11\overline{)121}$

DIVISION 6 TO 12

Name: ____________________
Date: __________ Time: __________

Score: /50

1. $8\overline{)32}$	2. $7\overline{)126}$	3. $8\overline{)128}$	4. $7\overline{)35}$	5. $6\overline{)42}$
6. $9\overline{)99}$	7. $6\overline{)78}$	8. $6\overline{)36}$	9. $8\overline{)88}$	10. $7\overline{)42}$
11. $9\overline{)45}$	12. $11\overline{)55}$	13. $10\overline{)70}$	14. $9\overline{)81}$	15. $10\overline{)50}$
16. $6\overline{)42}$	17. $9\overline{)126}$	18. $7\overline{)140}$	19. $10\overline{)100}$	20. $8\overline{)24}$
21. $9\overline{)144}$	22. $10\overline{)110}$	23. $8\overline{)128}$	24. $9\overline{)54}$	25. $12\overline{)24}$
26. $9\overline{)117}$	27. $7\overline{)49}$	28. $11\overline{)44}$	29. $7\overline{)112}$	30. $7\overline{)35}$
31. $11\overline{)55}$	32. $7\overline{)119}$	33. $7\overline{)70}$	34. $10\overline{)110}$	35. $7\overline{)49}$
36. $8\overline{)56}$	37. $10\overline{)70}$	38. $11\overline{)55}$	39. $9\overline{)108}$	40. $8\overline{)24}$
41. $10\overline{)130}$	42. $8\overline{)48}$	43. $7\overline{)91}$	44. $9\overline{)117}$	45. $8\overline{)72}$
46. $8\overline{)48}$	47. $9\overline{)126}$	48. $11\overline{)88}$	49. $11\overline{)22}$	50. $9\overline{)117}$

DIVISION 6 TO 12

Name: ____________________

Date: __________ Time: __________

Score: /50

1. $11 \overline{)143}$	2. $7 \overline{)105}$	3. $6 \overline{)36}$	4. $12 \overline{)108}$	5. $7 \overline{)168}$
6. $11 \overline{)88}$	7. $8 \overline{)96}$	8. $11 \overline{)121}$	9. $11 \overline{)176}$	10. $11 \overline{)22}$
11. $11 \overline{)22}$	12. $9 \overline{)90}$	13. $7 \overline{)28}$	14. $6 \overline{)102}$	15. $10 \overline{)40}$
16. $8 \overline{)112}$	17. $8 \overline{)104}$	18. $10 \overline{)120}$	19. $8 \overline{)96}$	20. $6 \overline{)114}$
21. $11 \overline{)99}$	22. $7 \overline{)133}$	23. $12 \overline{)192}$	24. $11 \overline{)99}$	25. $8 \overline{)168}$
26. $8 \overline{)56}$	27. $10 \overline{)170}$	28. $10 \overline{)80}$	29. $12 \overline{)60}$	30. $8 \overline{)40}$
31. $9 \overline{)27}$	32. $11 \overline{)44}$	33. $10 \overline{)180}$	34. $6 \overline{)24}$	35. $6 \overline{)180}$
36. $7 \overline{)98}$	37. $7 \overline{)112}$	38. $9 \overline{)144}$	39. $9 \overline{)135}$	40. $6 \overline{)162}$
41. $10 \overline{)100}$	42. $12 \overline{)156}$	43. $11 \overline{)66}$	44. $11 \overline{)66}$	45. $8 \overline{)120}$
46. $10 \overline{)90}$	47. $11 \overline{)110}$	48. $10 \overline{)100}$	49. $10 \overline{)60}$	50. $7 \overline{)189}$

DIVISION 6 TO 12

Name: ____________________

Date: ________ Time: ________

Score: /50

1. $11\overline{)132}$	2. $12\overline{)96}$	3. $7\overline{)119}$	4. $12\overline{)24}$	5. $11\overline{)22}$
6. $12\overline{)24}$	7. $10\overline{)80}$	8. $11\overline{)176}$	9. $11\overline{)176}$	10. $9\overline{)72}$
11. $9\overline{)45}$	12. $9\overline{)99}$	13. $11\overline{)88}$	14. $6\overline{)156}$	15. $11\overline{)198}$
16. $10\overline{)170}$	17. $8\overline{)48}$	18. $7\overline{)140}$	19. $10\overline{)150}$	20. $8\overline{)96}$
21. $8\overline{)48}$	22. $7\overline{)70}$	23. $7\overline{)147}$	24. $11\overline{)110}$	25. $6\overline{)174}$
26. $11\overline{)176}$	27. $10\overline{)190}$	28. $11\overline{)165}$	29. $9\overline{)81}$	30. $11\overline{)88}$
31. $8\overline{)128}$	32. $8\overline{)24}$	33. $10\overline{)50}$	34. $10\overline{)30}$	35. $7\overline{)105}$
36. $9\overline{)81}$	37. $10\overline{)190}$	38. $6\overline{)54}$	39. $12\overline{)180}$	40. $8\overline{)72}$
41. $8\overline{)184}$	42. $10\overline{)30}$	43. $7\overline{)49}$	44. $10\overline{)190}$	45. $9\overline{)189}$
46. $10\overline{)100}$	47. $8\overline{)40}$	48. $7\overline{)98}$	49. $6\overline{)54}$	50. $8\overline{)64}$

DIVISION 6 TO 12

Name: ____________________

Date: __________ Time: __________

Score: /50

1. $8\overline{)56}$	2. $9\overline{)72}$	3. $12\overline{)60}$	4. $7\overline{)140}$	5. $11\overline{)110}$
6. $11\overline{)176}$	7. $8\overline{)176}$	8. $9\overline{)54}$	9. $12\overline{)180}$	10. $12\overline{)36}$
11. $8\overline{)32}$	12. $9\overline{)162}$	13. $8\overline{)192}$	14. $7\overline{)119}$	15. $9\overline{)189}$
16. $9\overline{)54}$	17. $9\overline{)144}$	18. $10\overline{)140}$	19. $8\overline{)56}$	20. $9\overline{)117}$
21. $10\overline{)30}$	22. $12\overline{)84}$	23. $8\overline{)144}$	24. $11\overline{)154}$	25. $9\overline{)198}$
26. $11\overline{)66}$	27. $7\overline{)91}$	28. $12\overline{)84}$	29. $6\overline{)156}$	30. $8\overline{)168}$
31. $10\overline{)90}$	32. $8\overline{)24}$	33. $12\overline{)168}$	34. $8\overline{)96}$	35. $7\overline{)112}$
36. $11\overline{)176}$	37. $12\overline{)48}$	38. $12\overline{)108}$	39. $8\overline{)64}$	40. $9\overline{)153}$
41. $10\overline{)160}$	42. $11\overline{)143}$	43. $11\overline{)88}$	44. $12\overline{)60}$	45. $10\overline{)140}$
46. $11\overline{)132}$	47. $12\overline{)24}$	48. $6\overline{)114}$	49. $9\overline{)90}$	50. $10\overline{)160}$

COLORING ACTIVITY

WORD PROBLEMS

DIVISION 6 TO 12

Name: ____________________

Date: __________ Time: __________

1. If 100 cars outside the mall are parked in 10 equal rows, how many cars are in each row?

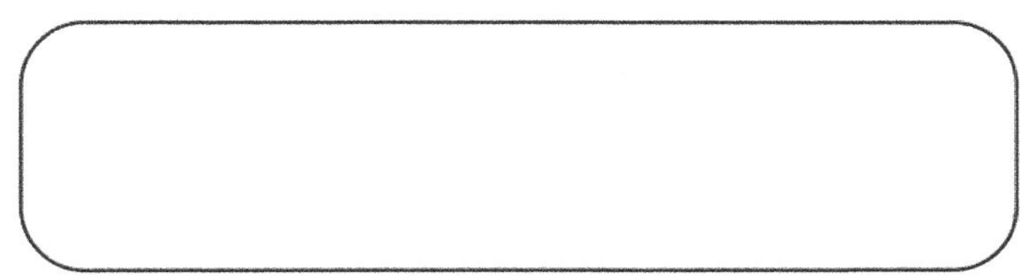

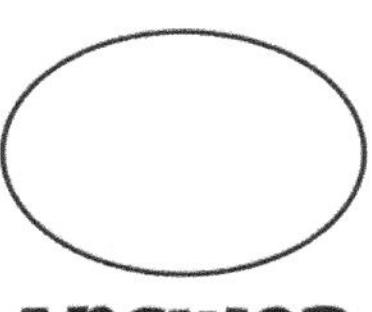

ANSWER

2. If 120 tiles on the floor in the hallway are installed in 12 equal rows, how many tiles are in each row?

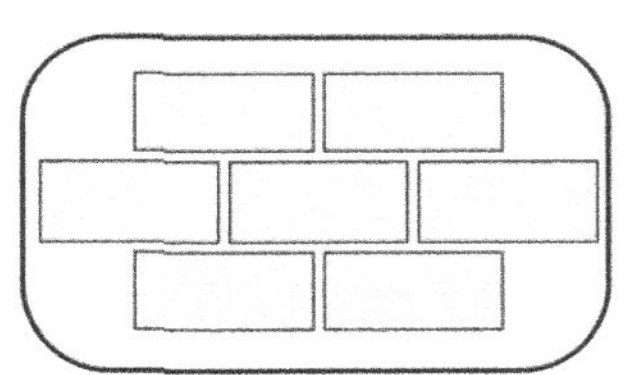

ANSWER

3. In the garden, there are 12 rows with the same number of pumpkins in each row. If there are 108 pumpkins all together, how many pumpkins are in each row?

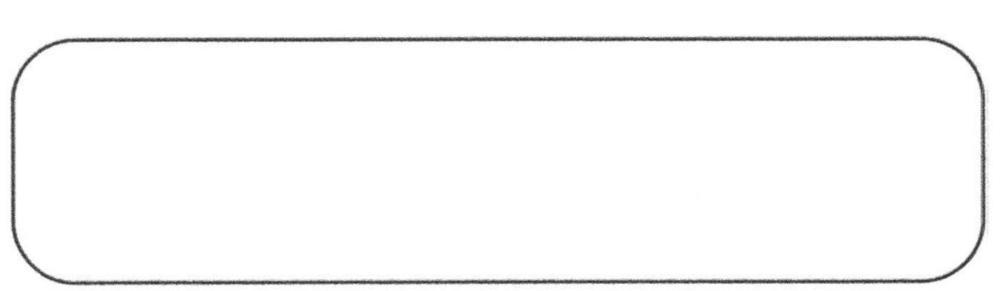

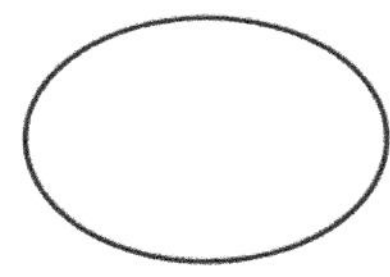

ANSWER

4. If 99 grape vines in the orchard are planted in 9 equal rows, how many grape vines are in each row?

ANSWER

WORD PROBLEMS
DIVISION 6 TO 12

Name: ____________________
Date: __________ Time: __________

5. If 88 boxes of nails at the home improvement store are organized in 11 equal rows, how many boxes of nails are in each row?

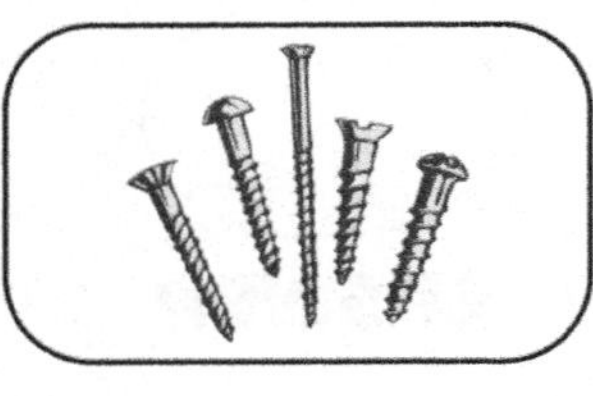
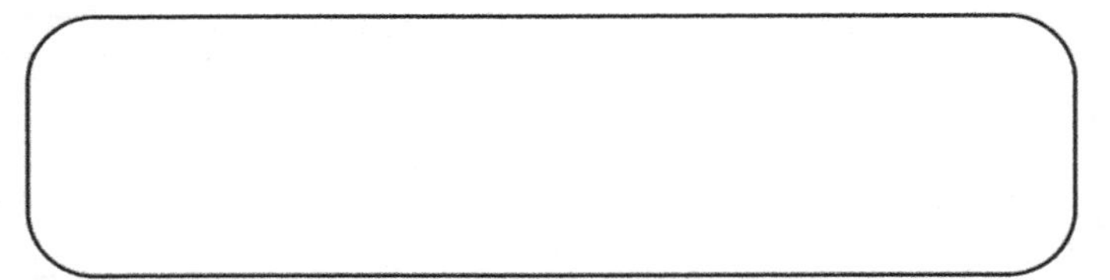
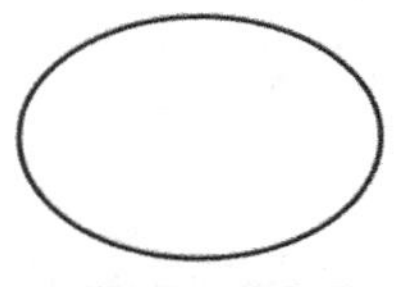
ANSWER

6. On the table at the fruit stand, there are 5 rows with the same number of pears in each row. If there are 55 pears all together, how many pears are in each row?

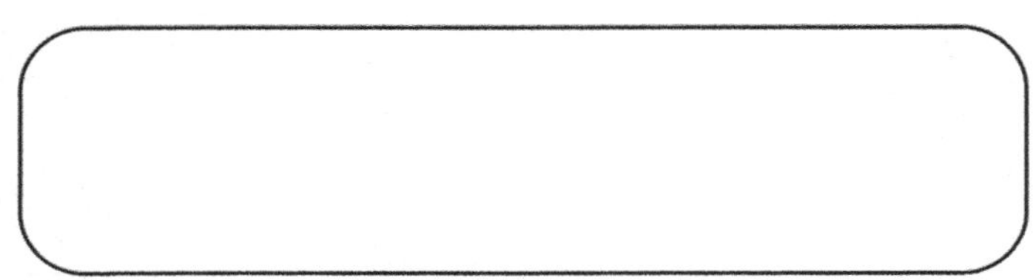
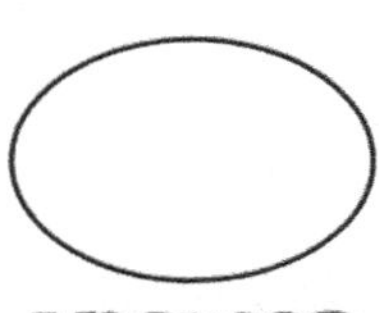
ANSWER

7. On the grocery shelf, there are 6 rows with the same cans of soup in each row. If there are 60 cans of soup all together, how many cans of soup are in each row?

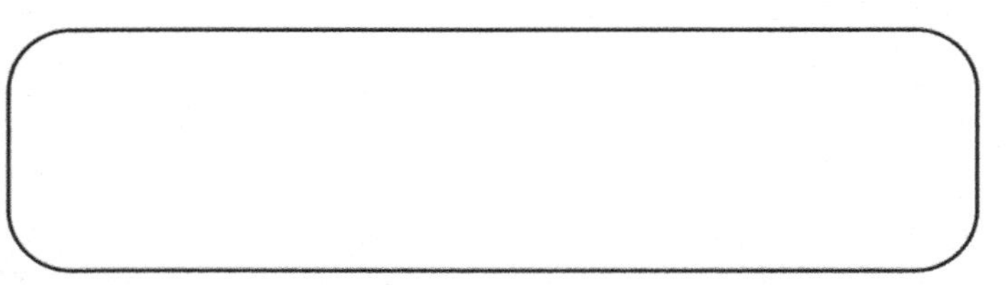
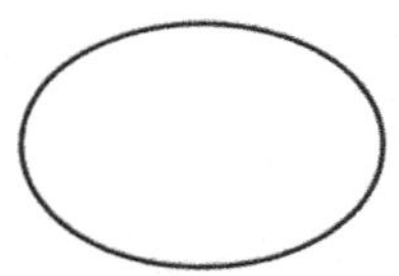
ANSWER

8. In a jewelry store, there are 9 rows of diamond rings in each row. If there are 90 diamond rings all together, how many diamond rings are in each row?

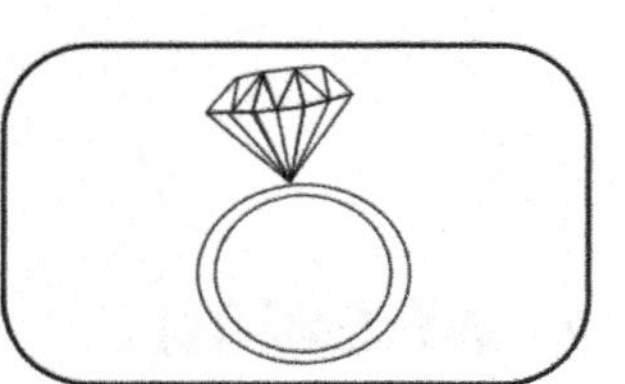

ANSWER

WORD PROBLEMS
DIVISION 6 TO 12

Name: ____________________

Date: __________ Time: __________

9. If 33 students in the marching band are standing in 3 equal rows, how many students are in each row?

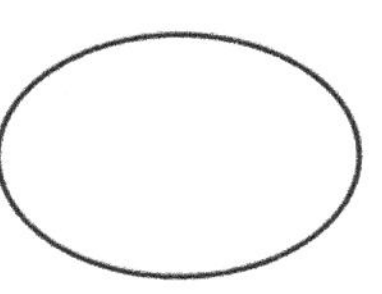

ANSWER

10. In the garden, there are 10 rows with the same number of squash in each row. If there are 130 squash all together, how many squash are in each row?

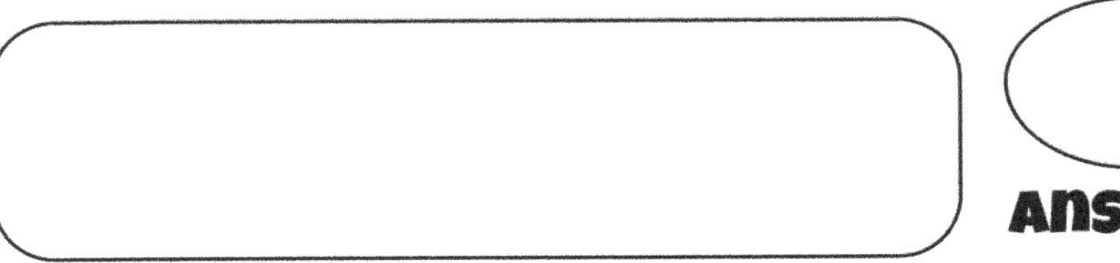

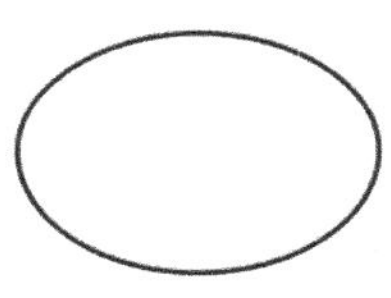

ANSWER

11. There are 9 times as many blue jays in the low tree as there are in the high tree. There are 108 blue jays in the low tree. How many blue jays are in the high tree?

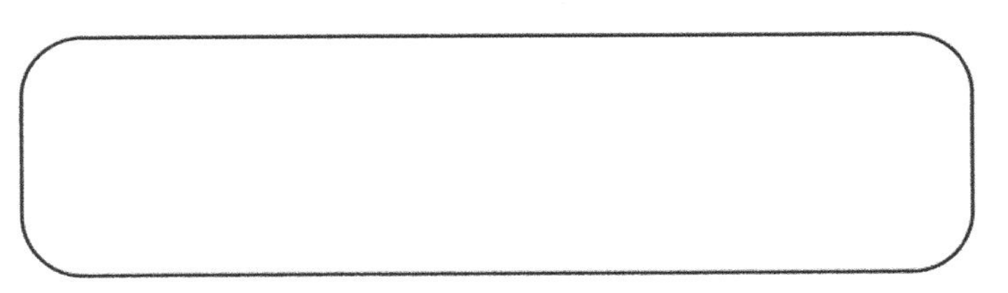

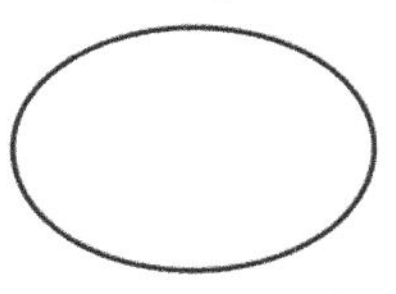

ANSWER

12. There are 7 times as many kids on the round table as there are on the square table. There are 84 kids on the round table. How many kids are on the square table?

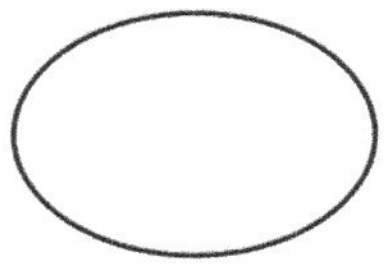

ANSWER

ACTIVITY CORNER

DIVIDE THE NUMBERS

84 ÷ 12 =

110 ÷ 11 =

80 ÷ 10 =

60 ÷ 12 =

WORD PROBLEMS
DIVISION 6 TO 12

Name: ____________________
Date: __________ Time: __________

13. Lucy baked some cookies. Mike baked 12 times as many cookies. Mike baked 60 cookies. How many cookies did Lucy bake?

Answer

14. There are 6 times as many students on the ○ table as there are on the □ table. There are 12 students on the ○ table. How many students are on the □ table?

Answer

15. Luke gathered some pine cones. Helen gathered 9 times as many pine cones. Helen gathered 108 pine cones. How many pine cones did Luke gather?

Answer

16. Sage bought some sour candies. Penny bought 10 times as many sour candies. Penny bought 70 sour candies. How many sour candies did Sage buy?

Answer

WORD PROBLEMS
DIVISION 6 TO 12

Name: ____________________

Date: __________ Time: __________

17. There are 5 times as many blue jays in the low tree as there are in the high tree. There are 11 blue jays in the low tree. How many blue jays are in the high tree?

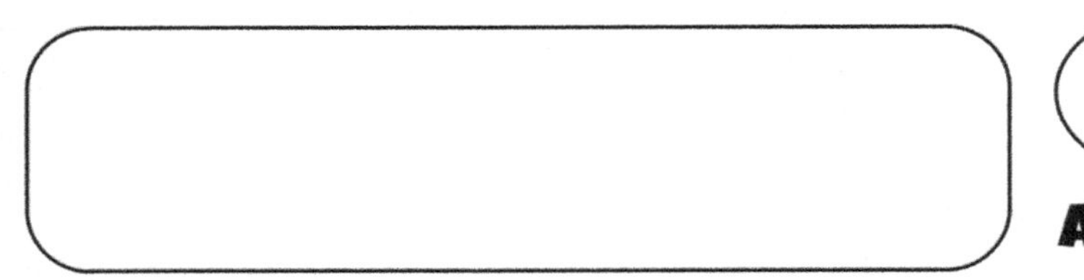

Answer

18. Mike wrote some short stories. Grace wrote 8 times as many short stories. Grace wrote 72 short stories. How many short stories did Mike write?

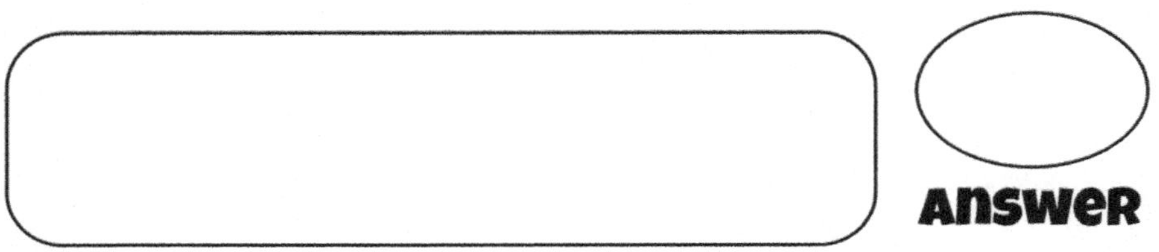

Answer

19. There are 7 times as many nickels in the purple box as there are in the yellow box. There are 77 nickels in the purple box. How many nickels are in the yellow box?

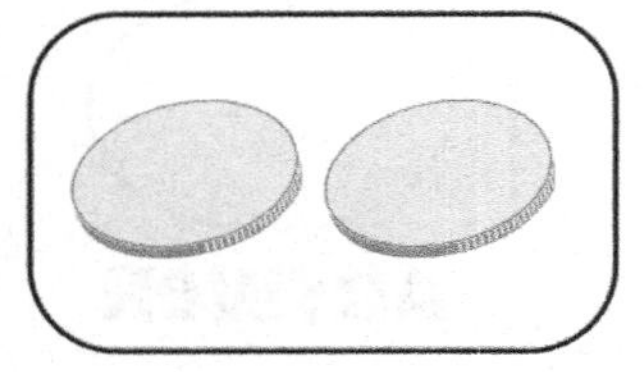

Answer

20. Jim gathered some pine cones. Owen gathered 2 times as many pine cones. Owen gathered 22 pine cones. How many pine cones did Jim gather?

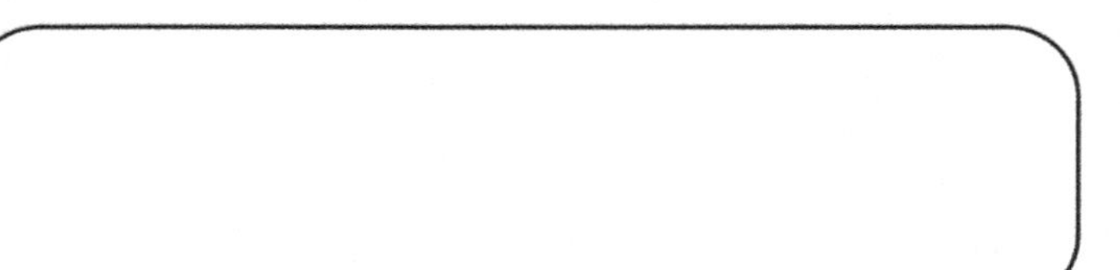

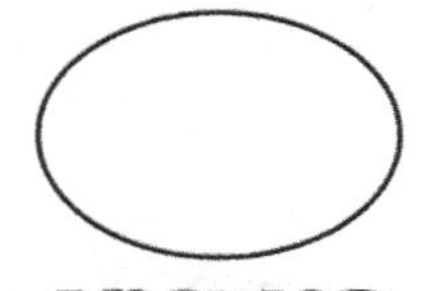

Answer

WORD PROBLEMS
DIVISION 6 TO 12

Name: ____________________

Date: __________ Time: __________

21. What is 110 divided by 10?

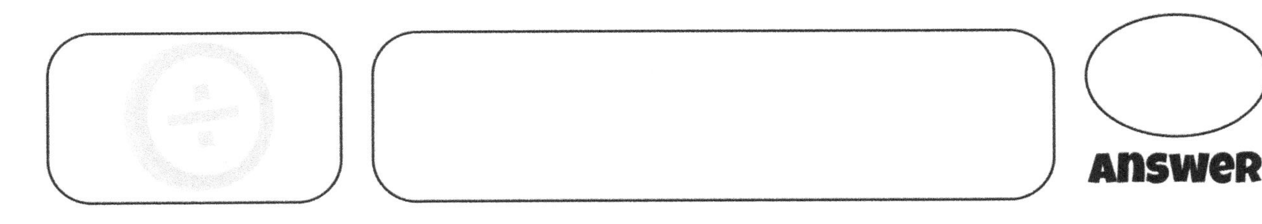

22. What is 81 divided by 9?

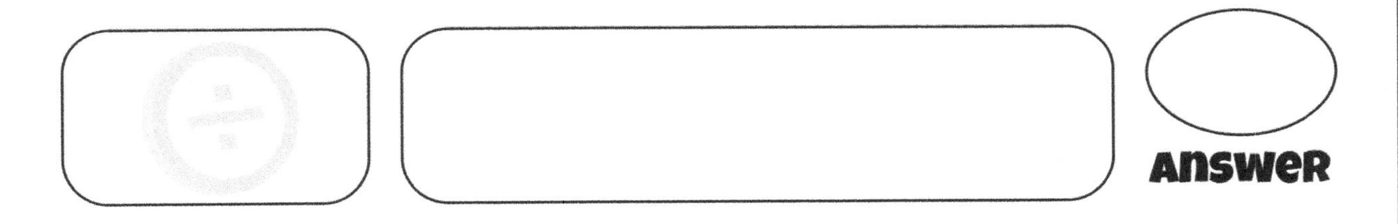

23. What is 150 divided by 10?

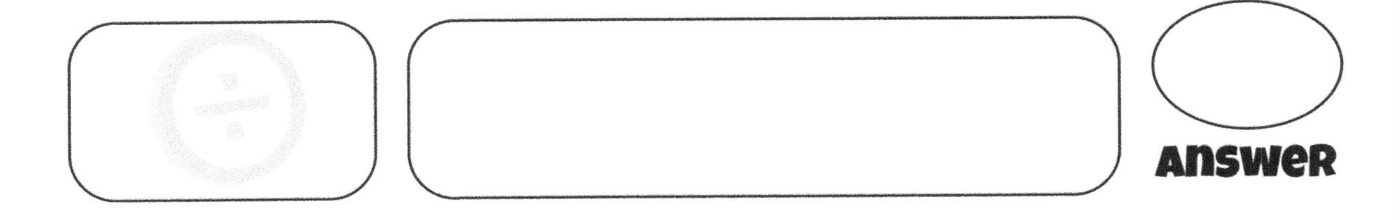

24. What is 11 divided by 1?

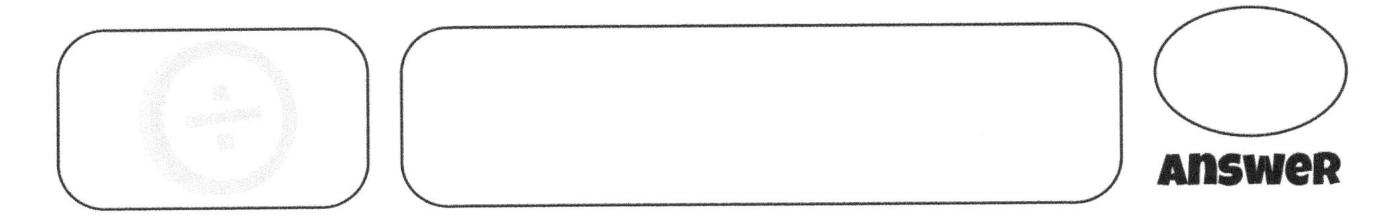

WORD PROBLEMS
DIVISION 6 TO 12

Name: ____________________

Date: __________ Time: __________

25. What is 60 divided by 6?

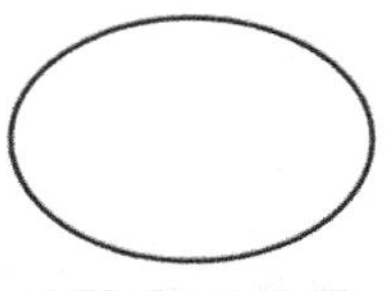

ANSWER

ACTIVITY CORNER

CONNECT THE DOTS

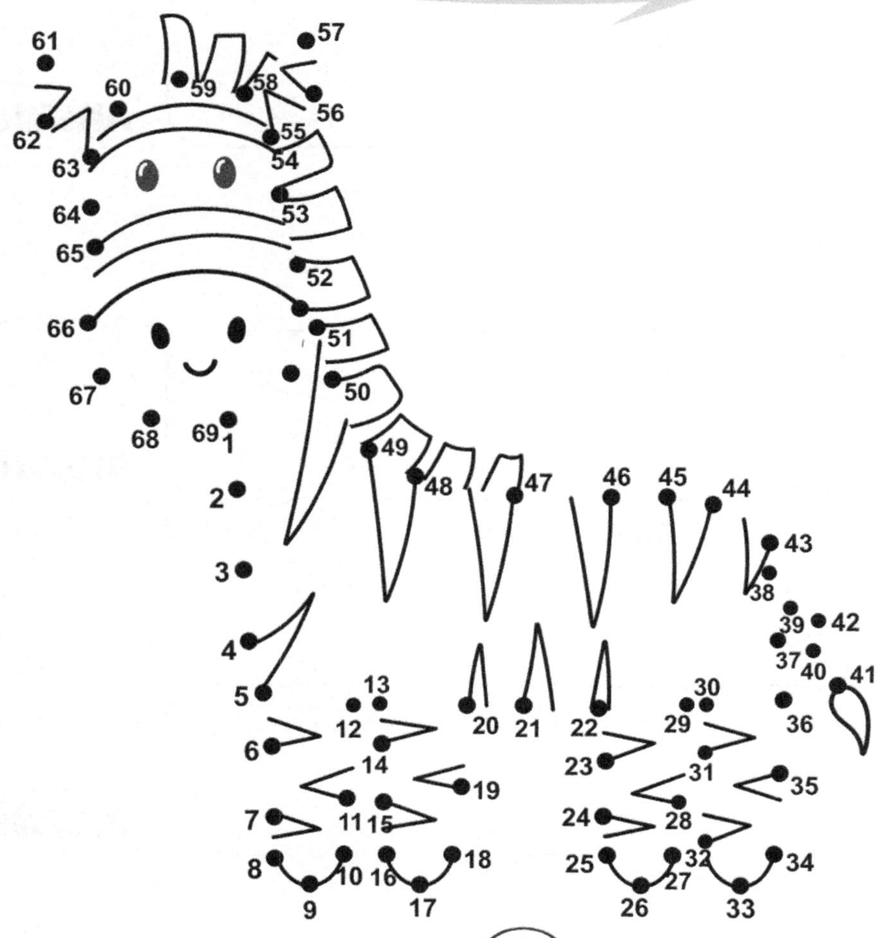

DIVISION 9 TO 12

Name: ______________________
Date: __________ Time: __________

1. 12) 108	2. 10) 50	3. 11) 99	4. 10) 80	5. 10) 80
6. 10) 110	7. 10) 110	8. 11) 110	9. 10) 90	10. 11) 11
11. 10) 50	12. 12) 108	13. 11) 66	14. 11) 33	15. 11) 88
16. 12) 48	17. 9) 108	18. 11) 44	19. 10) 80	20. 10) 20
21. 10) 10	22. 10) 60	23. 11) 55	24. 11) 66	25. 12) 36
26. 11) 33	27. 11) 99	28. 10) 80	29. 9) 54	30. 12) 48
31. 11) 66	32. 10) 90	33. 11) 88	34. 11) 11	35. 9) 45
36. 11) 88	37. 9) 45	38. 11) 33	39. 11) 88	40. 12) 84
41. 11) 99	42. 11) 22	43. 9) 90	44. 9) 90	45. 11) 11
46. 10) 70	47. 10) 40	48. 9) 9	49. 10) 20	50. 11) 66

DIVISION 9 TO 12

Name: ____________________

Date: __________ Time: __________

Score: /50

1. 10) 70	2. 12) 24	3. 10) 20	4. 11) 110	5. 12) 12
6. 9) 45	7. 9) 72	8. 9) 81	9. 10) 80	10. 9) 72
11. 10) 10	12. 12) 12	13. 12) 72	14. 10) 50	15. 10) 10
16. 11) 55	17. 10) 40	18. 10) 80	19. 11) 33	20. 12) 84
21. 12) 72	22. 10) 10	23. 10) 50	24. 11) 33	25. 10) 60
26. 9) 27	27. 9) 90	28. 11) 22	29. 10) 20	30. 12) 108
31. 12) 12	32. 12) 60	33. 10) 70	34. 11) 33	35. 11) 110
36. 11) 66	37. 10) 60	38. 11) 22	39. 11) 44	40. 12) 96
41. 9) 99	42. 11) 44	43. 11) 88	44. 10) 20	45. 11) 66
46. 12) 60	47. 10) 50	48. 11) 66	49. 12) 84	50. 12) 72

DIVISION 9 TO 12

Name: ______________________

Date: __________ Time: __________

Score: /50

1. 10)70	2. 11)55	3. 11)11	4. 11)66	5. 11)110
6. 11)66	7. 11)99	8. 11)99	9. 11)11	10. 11)99
11. 12)12	12. 10)60	13. 10)80	14. 10)90	15. 10)110
16. 10)70	17. 11)99	18. 10)50	19. 11)99	20. 11)88
21. 10)50	22. 10)40	23. 10)100	24. 11)66	25. 9)27
26. 9)81	27. 12)84	28. 11)66	29. 9)45	30. 11)110
31. 10)20	32. 9)54	33. 11)88	34. 11)22	35. 12)36
36. 9)108	37. 11)110	38. 10)20	39. 10)110	40. 11)33
41. 10)100	42. 11)22	43. 12)48	44. 10)60	45. 9)72
46. 9)54	47. 10)50	48. 10)80	49. 11)99	50. 11)44

DIVISION 9 TO 12

Name: ____________________

Date: __________ Time: __________

Score: /50

1. 9)36	2. 11)110	3. 10)40	4. 11)66	5. 9)36
6. 12)72	7. 10)50	8. 11)44	9. 12)60	10. 11)11
11. 9)99	12. 12)108	13. 9)99	14. 10)100	15. 10)60
16. 11)44	17. 10)30	18. 12)12	19. 10)10	20. 9)108
21. 11)110	22. 10)80	23. 10)50	24. 10)40	25. 12)84
26. 11)44	27. 11)77	28. 10)40	29. 10)40	30. 10)110
31. 10)60	32. 12)48	33. 12)108	34. 10)70	35. 12)48
36. 12)108	37. 12)84	38. 10)110	39. 10)10	40. 11)55
41. 10)120	42. 11)77	43. 9)63	44. 11)77	45. 11)99
46. 12)0	47. 12)12	48. 10)60	49. 10)60	50. 12)24

DIVISION 9 TO 12

Name: ____________________

Date: __________ Time: __________

Score: /50

1. $9\overline{)63}$	2. $9\overline{)90}$	3. $12\overline{)72}$	4. $9\overline{)108}$	5. $12\overline{)84}$
6. $12\overline{)108}$	7. $11\overline{)44}$	8. $10\overline{)20}$	9. $9\overline{)27}$	10. $12\overline{)36}$
11. $11\overline{)11}$	12. $11\overline{)88}$	13. $10\overline{)100}$	14. $11\overline{)99}$	15. $12\overline{)84}$
16. $11\overline{)77}$	17. $12\overline{)108}$	18. $11\overline{)11}$	19. $11\overline{)22}$	20. $9\overline{)36}$
21. $10\overline{)10}$	22. $11\overline{)55}$	23. $9\overline{)18}$	24. $11\overline{)66}$	25. $11\overline{)99}$
26. $10\overline{)100}$	27. $10\overline{)70}$	28. $11\overline{)88}$	29. $12\overline{)84}$	30. $12\overline{)36}$
31. $11\overline{)44}$	32. $11\overline{)22}$	33. $10\overline{)80}$	34. $10\overline{)70}$	35. $11\overline{)99}$
36. $10\overline{)110}$	37. $11\overline{)110}$	38. $12\overline{)96}$	39. $12\overline{)96}$	40. $10\overline{)50}$
41. $12\overline{)72}$	42. $10\overline{)110}$	43. $10\overline{)70}$	44. $10\overline{)50}$	45. $11\overline{)110}$
46. $11\overline{)33}$	47. $11\overline{)110}$	48. $9\overline{)81}$	49. $11\overline{)11}$	50. $12\overline{)36}$

DIVISION 9 TO 12

Name: ______________________

Date: __________ Time: __________

Score: /50

1. $11\overline{)77}$	2. $11\overline{)55}$	3. $12\overline{)72}$	4. $12\overline{)72}$	5. $12\overline{)72}$
6. $10\overline{)60}$	7. $11\overline{)44}$	8. $11\overline{)55}$	9. $11\overline{)99}$	10. $12\overline{)60}$
11. $10\overline{)30}$	12. $10\overline{)40}$	13. $10\overline{)110}$	14. $9\overline{)54}$	15. $11\overline{)44}$
16. $11\overline{)110}$	17. $12\overline{)36}$	18. $11\overline{)0}$	19. $10\overline{)30}$	20. $10\overline{)110}$
21. $11\overline{)22}$	22. $9\overline{)9}$	23. $11\overline{)33}$	24. $9\overline{)18}$	25. $9\overline{)36}$
26. $11\overline{)99}$	27. $9\overline{)81}$	28. $11\overline{)110}$	29. $10\overline{)50}$	30. $10\overline{)10}$
31. $10\overline{)100}$	32. $10\overline{)110}$	33. $9\overline{)81}$	34. $10\overline{)30}$	35. $10\overline{)60}$
36. $10\overline{)110}$	37. $10\overline{)20}$	38. $10\overline{)80}$	39. $12\overline{)24}$	40. $10\overline{)20}$
41. $10\overline{)110}$	42. $9\overline{)90}$	43. $12\overline{)108}$	44. $10\overline{)30}$	45. $9\overline{)27}$
46. $11\overline{)11}$	47. $11\overline{)110}$	48. $12\overline{)72}$	49. $10\overline{)20}$	50. $11\overline{)33}$

DIVISION 9 TO 12

Name: ____________________

Date: __________ Time: __________

Score: /50

1. 9)108	2. 9)9	3. 12)48	4. 11)22	5. 11)11
6. 12)60	7. 10)100	8. 11)110	9. 11)11	10. 10)50
11. 10)30	12. 10)80	13. 12)96	14. 12)72	15. 11)99
16. 10)100	17. 9)54	18. 11)77	19. 11)77	20. 10)20
21. 10)60	22. 9)27	23. 12)96	24. 11)11	25. 9)90
26. 10)60	27. 12)72	28. 12)84	29. 10)40	30. 11)77
31. 10)30	32. 12)72	33. 12)60	34. 10)100	35. 9)45
36. 9)18	37. 11)11	38. 9)36	39. 10)90	40. 9)99
41. 9)108	42. 10)80	43. 12)48	44. 11)11	45. 10)10
46. 11)55	47. 11)88	48. 10)50	49. 10)30	50. 9)63

DIVISION 9 TO 12

Name: ______________________

Date: __________ Time: __________

Score: /50

1. 10)80	2. 12)96	3. 10)110	4. 11)33	5. 11)66
6. 10)20	7. 11)44	8. 12)96	9. 11)33	10. 11)55
11. 11)99	12. 11)44	13. 9)72	14. 11)44	15. 11)33
16. 9)45	17. 10)40	18. 12)84	19. 10)100	20. 11)77
21. 12)36	22. 11)99	23. 11)77	24. 11)66	25. 12)84
26. 9)54	27. 11)11	28. 10)30	29. 11)77	30. 10)70
31. 12)108	32. 11)77	33. 11)66	34. 10)10	35. 10)80
36. 10)50	37. 10)10	38. 9)27	39. 11)22	40. 11)88
41. 12)84	42. 11)110	43. 10)20	44. 10)20	45. 10)110
46. 10)40	47. 10)110	48. 9)81	49. 10)90	50. 10)20

FIND THE 10 DIFFERENCES

WORD PROBLEMS
DIVISION 0 TO 12

Name: ______________________

Date: __________ Time: __________

1. Alan bought 7 candy bars. Max bought 4 times as many candy bars. How many candy bars did Max buy?

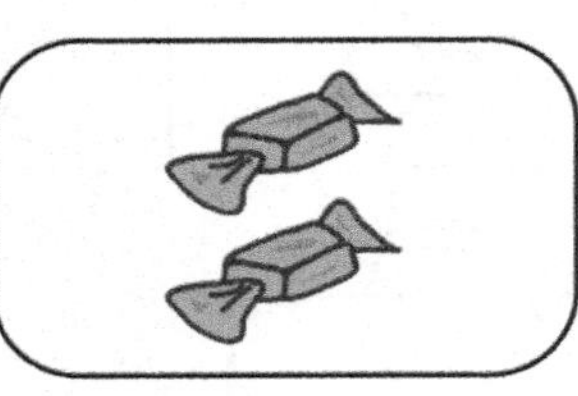
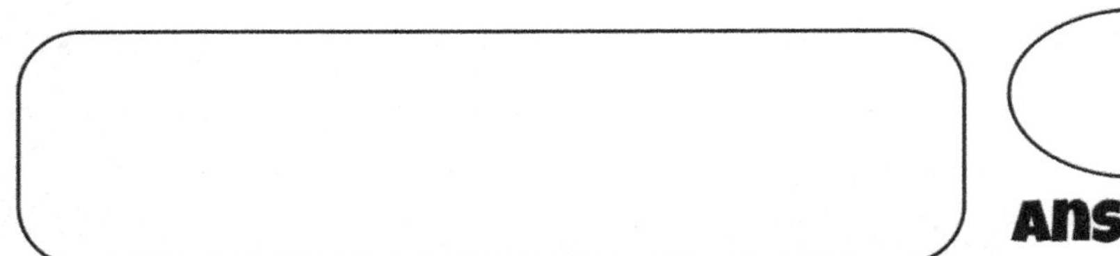

Answer

2. There are 6 flowers in the small flower pot and 2 times that many in the large flower pot. How many flowers are in the large flower pots?

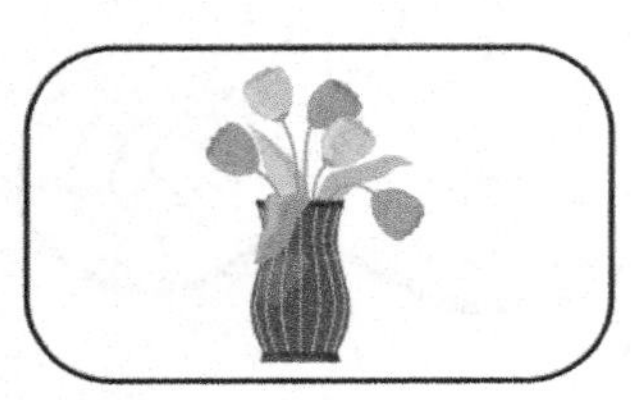

Answer

3. Each group in the gym has 2 kids. If there are 10 kids all together, how many groups are there?

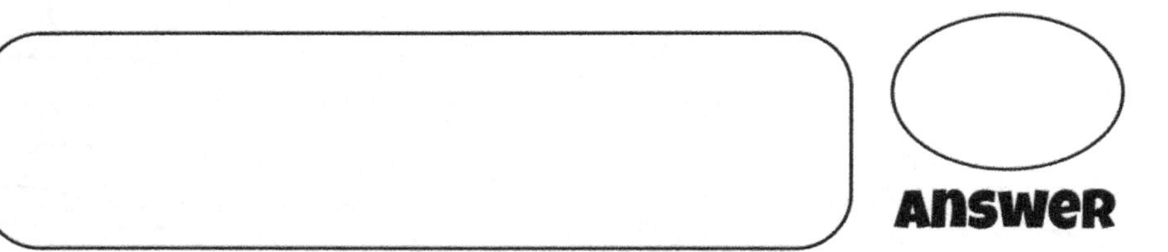

Answer

4. There are 40 balls on the short rack and 4 balls on the tall rack.
There are how many times as many balls on the short rack as on the tall rack?

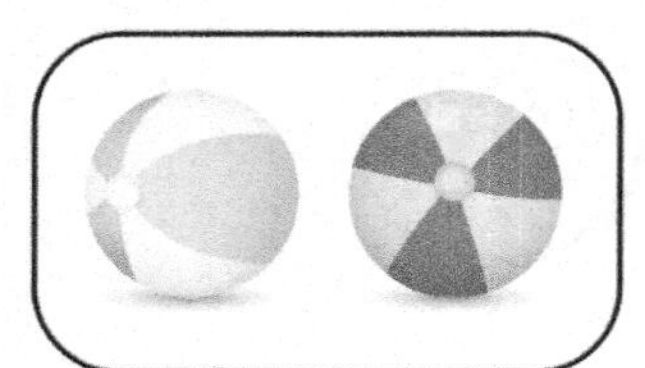

Answer

WORD PROBLEMS
DIVISION 0 TO 12

Name: ______________________

Date: __________ Time: __________

5. At the dry cleaners, there are 7 jackets in each row and there are 21 altogether. How many jackets are there in each row?

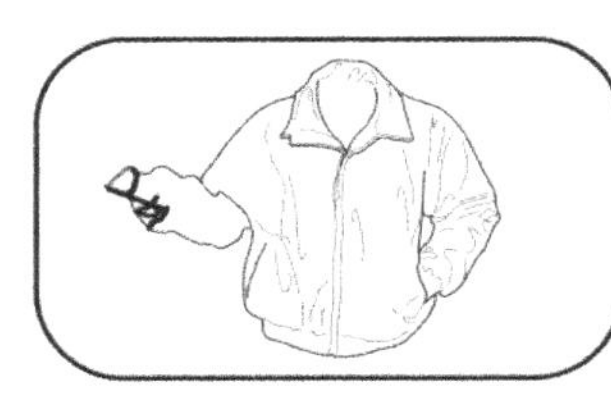
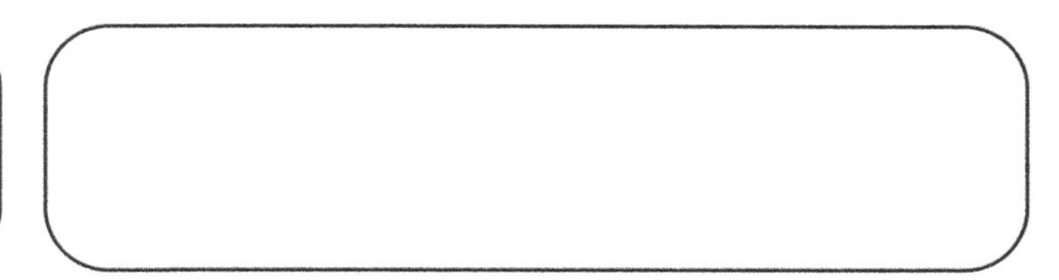
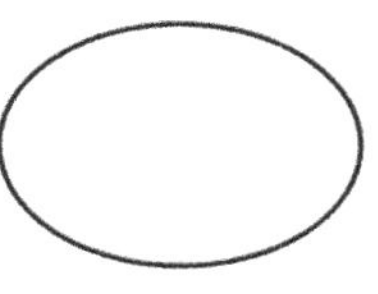

ANSWER

6. On the table at the fruit stand, there are 5 apples in each row and there are 15 fruits altogether. How many rows are there?

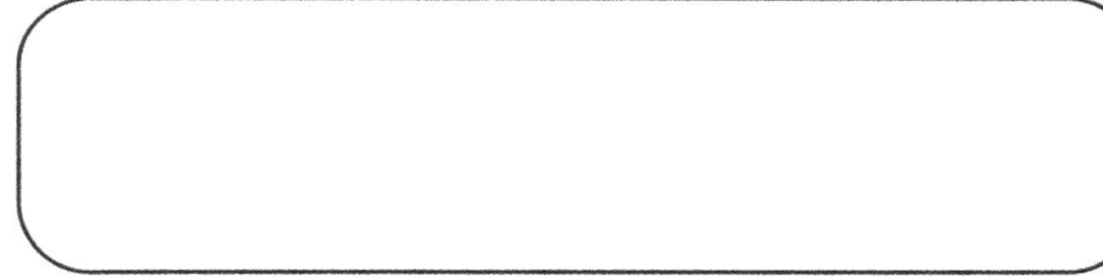
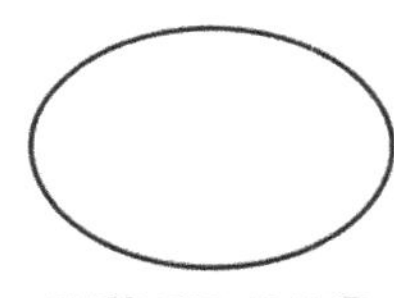

ANSWER

7. Sage painted 24 pictures for galleries. If there were 6 galleries, how many pictures did she paint for each gallery?

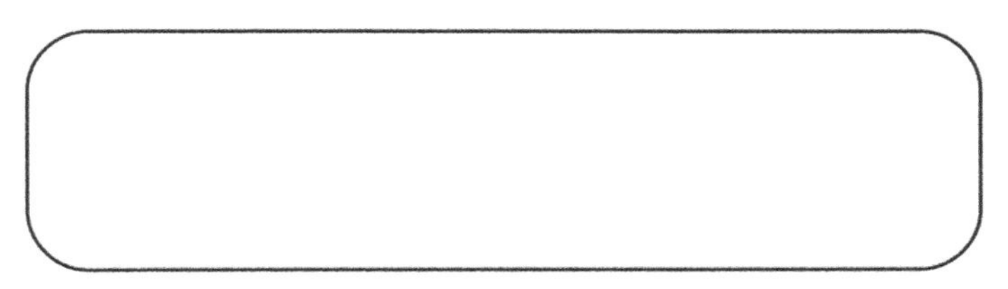
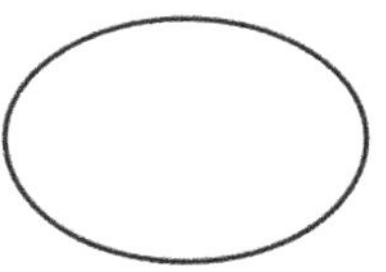

ANSWER

8. Ray put 10 cookies in containers. If there were 5 containers. How many cookies did he put in each container?

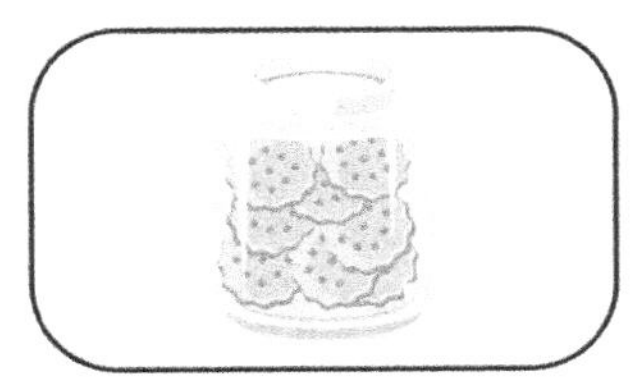
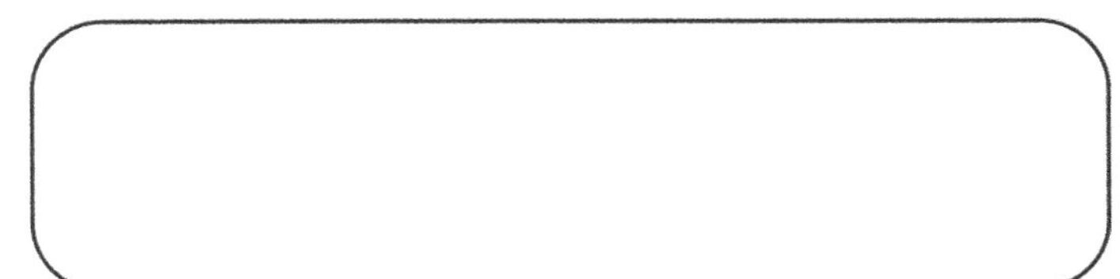
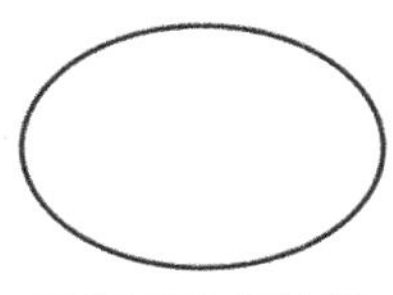

ANSWER

WORD PROBLEMS
DIVISION 0 TO 12

Name: ______________________
Date: __________ Time: __________

9. There are 6 times as many mobiles on shelf A as there are on shelf B. There are 12 mobiles on shelf A. How many mobiles are on shelf B?

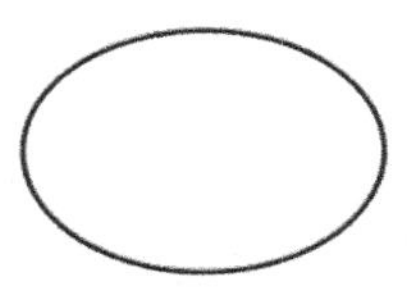

Answer

10. If 21 photographs on the bulletin board are lined up in 7 equal rows, how many photographs are in each row?

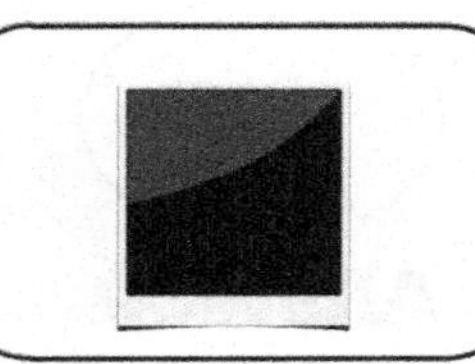
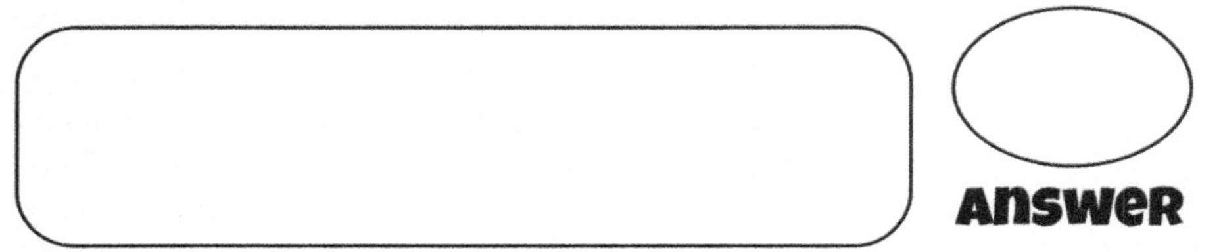

Answer

11. Deli's bakery sells 55 sandwiches in a 5- day week. Around how many sandwiches did Deli sell every day in a week?

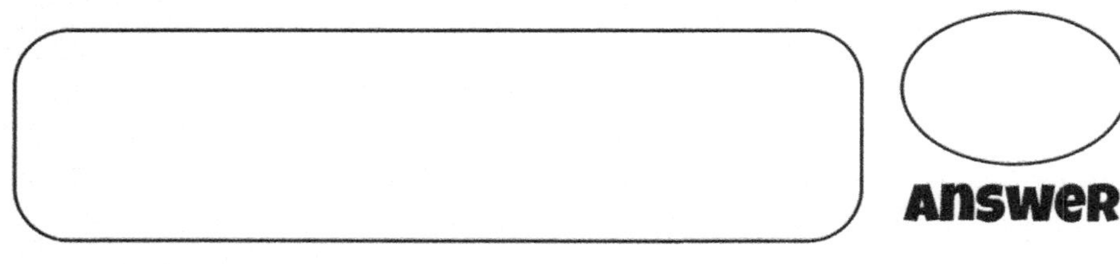

Answer

12. Joe's reading group 6 members. They have 54 books this year to read. How many books did each member read?

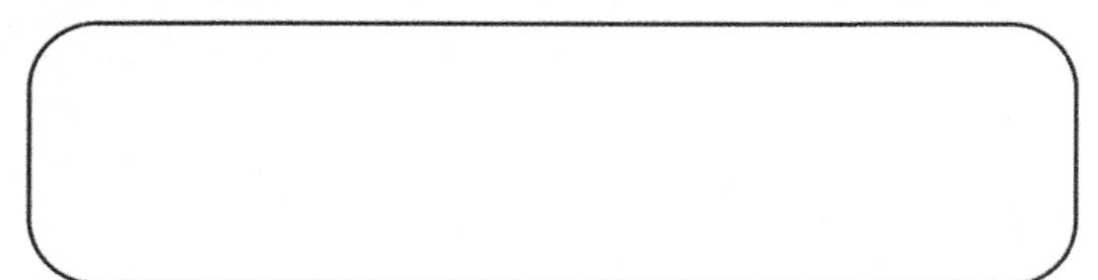

Answer

COLORING ACTIVITY

WORD PROBLEMS
DIVISION 0 TO 12

Name: ______________________

Date: __________ Time: __________

13. Danny celebrated his tenth birthday. He invited his friends and baked 64 Choco pies. He distributes the pies among his seven friends. How many did each get?

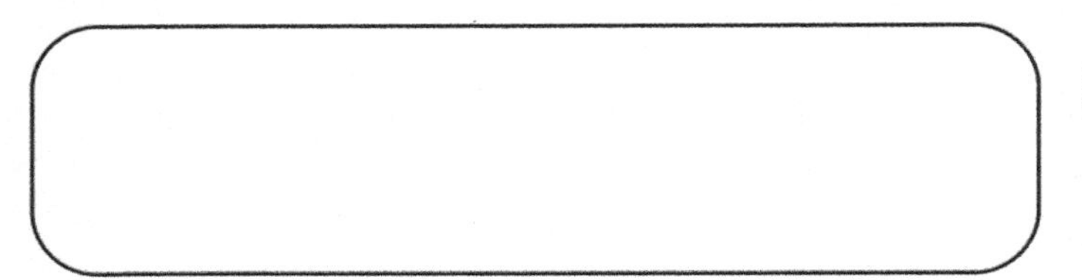

Answer

14. A baker makes 40 pastries and packs them all in a box. If each box holds 8 pastries, how many boxes of pastries he packed?

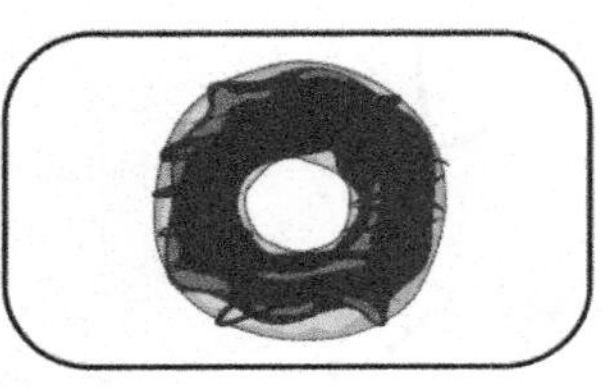

Answer

15. A group of 72 students were divided equally to participate in a marathon. Each team had 6 students. How many teams were there?

Answer

16. A tour operator planned for a trip for the tourists. There were 96 people in a tourist group. How many people were there in each group?

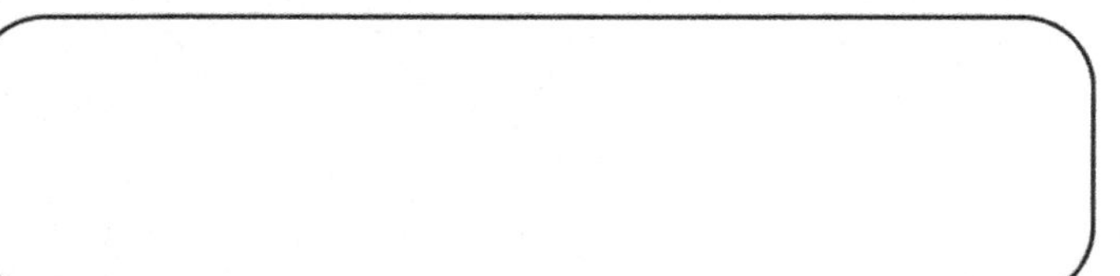

Answer

WORD PROBLEMS
DIVISION 0 TO 12

Name: ____________________
Date: __________ Time: __________

17. Emily has a collection of 49 science books. She puts an equal number of books in 7 shelves. How many books are there in each shelf?

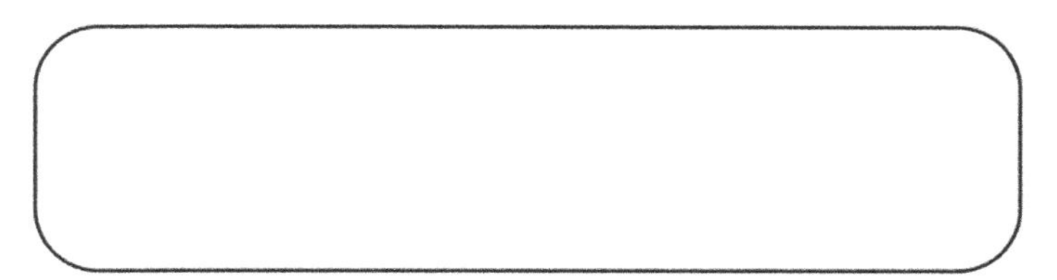

ANSWER

18. Mike rode his bike for 36 miles in 6 days. He covers the same distance everyday. How many miles did he ride each day?

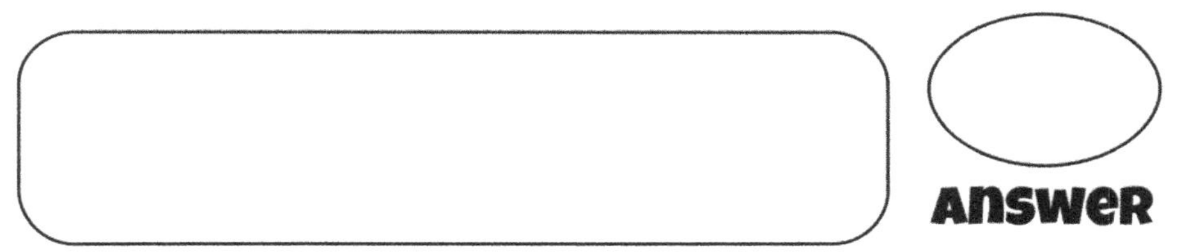

ANSWER

19. A fruit seller sold 81 melons in 9 days. How many melons did he sell each day?

ANSWER

20. Maggie stiches frocks for the sale. She uses 8 meters of cloth to stitch one frock. If she has 48 meters of cloth, how many frocks can she stitch in all?

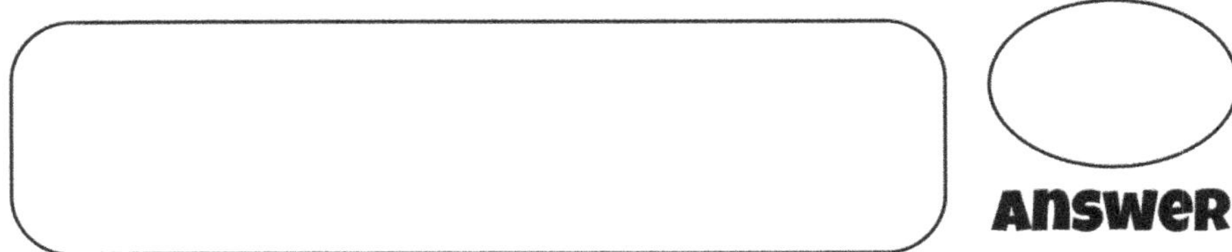

ANSWER

WORD PROBLEMS
DIVISION 0 TO 12

Name: ______________________
Date: __________ Time: __________

21. In a football field there were 120 people seated equally in 12 rows. How many people were seated in each row?

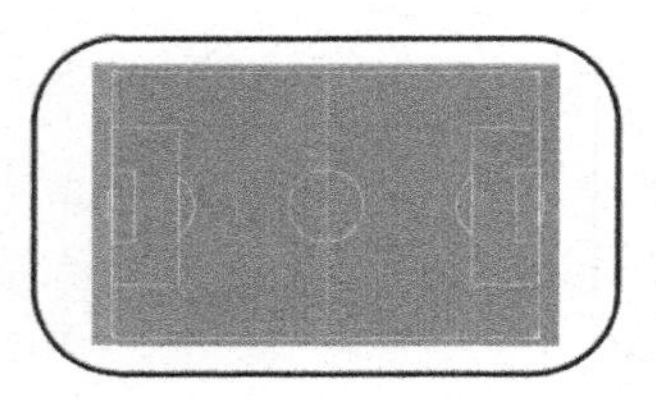

Answer

22. Ben had a collection of 144 crayons. He distributes it equally among his 12 friends. How many would each of his friends get?

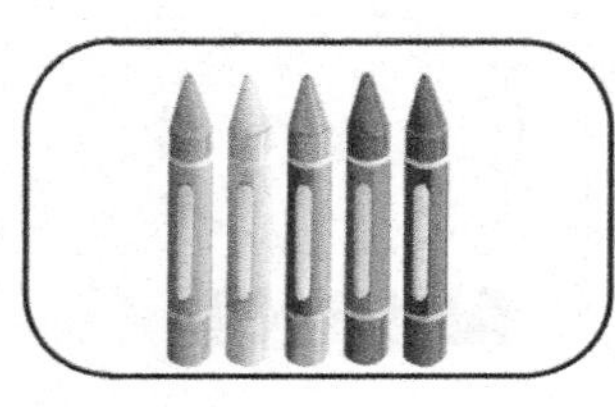
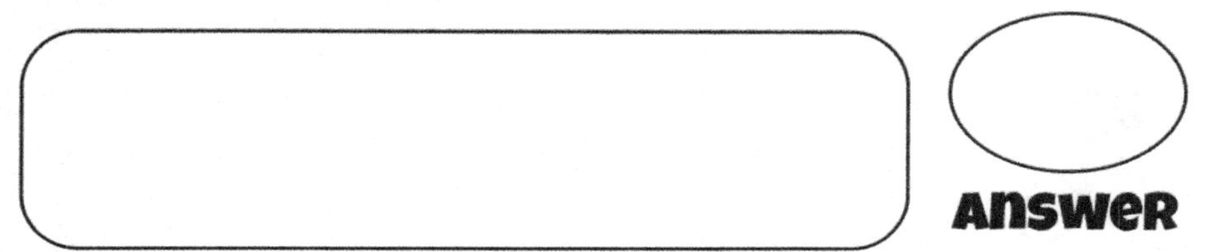

Answer

23. Carole invited 9 of her friends to a party. She has 18 cookies. How many cookies will each friend get?

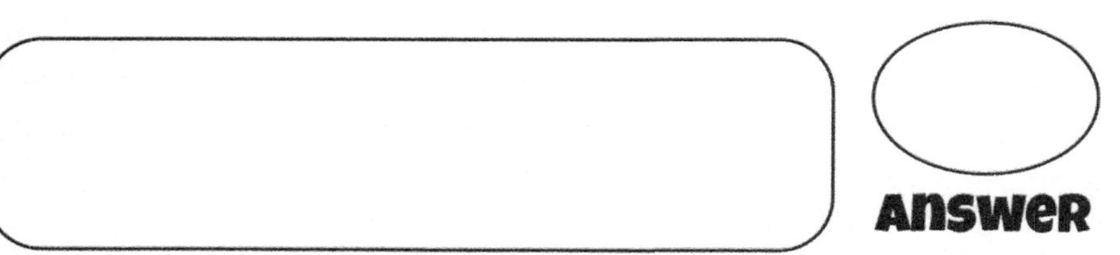

Answer

24. There were 11 students in the class and 99 blocks. How many would each student get and how many will be left over?

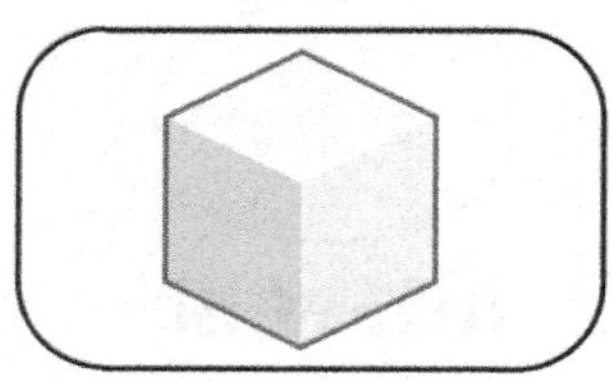
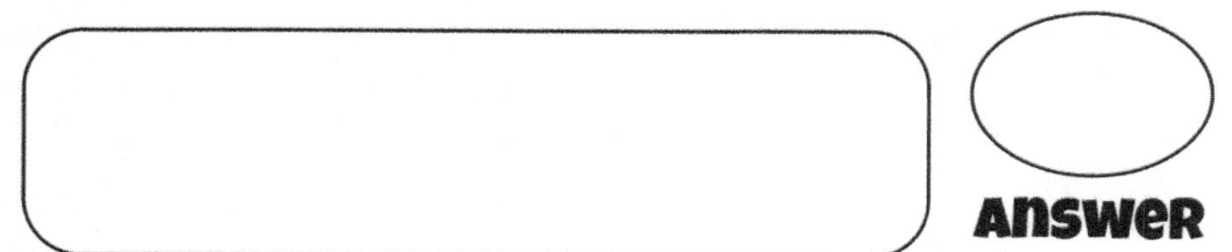

Answer

WORD PROBLEMS
DIVISION 0 TO 12

Name: ______________________

Date: __________ Time: __________

25. Merlin had a collection of 25 stamps. She packs it equally in 5 boxes. How many stamps will be there in each box?

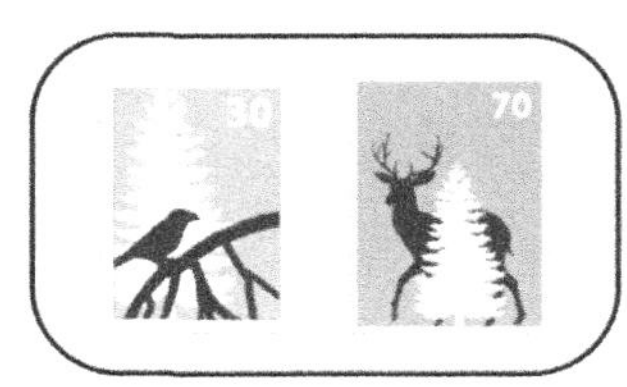

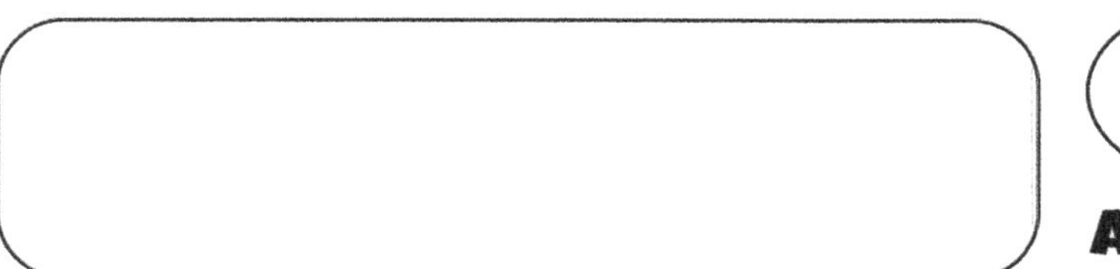

ANSWER

FIND A WAY

Answers for Word Problems

Multiplication 0 to 5

1. 6
2. 12
3. 8
4. 8
5. 16
6. 8
7. 12
8. 9
9. 9
10. 12
11. 6
12. 16
13. 6
14. 16
15. 8
16. 9
17. 8
18. 12
19. 6
20. 16
21. 4
22. 8
23. 12
24. 6
25. 9

Multiplication 5 to 8

1. 7
2. 10
3. 8
4. 9
5. 7
6. 6
7. 8
8. 10
9. 9
10. 7
11. 6
12. 8
13. 10
14. 8
15. 6
16. 7
17. 10
18. 9
19. 9
20. 7
21. 6
22. 8
23. 9
24. 10
25. 9

Answers for Word Problems

Multiplication 6 to 12

1. 11
2. 13
3. 15
4. 14
5. 12
6. 14
7. 11
8. 15
9. 13
10. 12
11. 14
12. 11
13. 15
14. 13
15. 15
16. 14
17. 12
18. 13
19. 14
20. 15
21. 11
22. 12
23. 14
24. 13
25. 15

Multiplication 0 to 12

1. 2
2. 3
3. 5
4. 4
5. 2
6. 4
7. 5
8. 3
9. 6
10. 8
11. 7
12. 10
13. 9
14. 8
15. 6
16. 7
17. 11
18. 12
19. 14
20. 13
21. 15
22. 12
23. 13
24. 14
25. 15

Answers for Word Problems

Division 0 to 4

1. 10
2. 6
3. 6
4. 10
5. 5
6. 10
7. 8
8. 9
9. 7
10. 5
11. 2
12. 4
13. 10
14. 7
15. 9
16. 5
17. 7
18. 8
19. 5
20. 9
21. 3
22. 8
23. 0
24. 0
25. 2

Division 5 to 8

1. 8
2. 8
3. 8
4. 9
5. 9
6. 7
7. 10
8. 9
9. 5
10. 3
11. 7
12. 8
13. 8
14. 7
15. 6
16. 10
17. 5
18. 9
19. 9
20. 6
21. 9
22. 10
23. 1
24. 8
25. 1

ANSWERS FOR WORD PROBLEMS

DIVISION 9 TO 12

1. 10
2. 10
3. 9
4. 11
5. 8
6. 11
7. 10
8. 10
9. 11
10. 12
11. 12
12. 12
13. 5
14. 2
15. 12
16. 7
17. 55
18. 9
19. 11
20. 11
21. 11
22. 9
23. 15
24. 11
25. 10

DIVISION 0 TO 12

1. 28
2. 12
3. 5
4. 10
5. 3
6. 3
7. 4
8. 2
9. 2
10. 3
11. 11
12. 9
13. 8
14. 5
15. 12
16. 8
17. 7
18. 6
19. 9
20. 6
21. 10
22. 12
23. 2
24. 9
25. 5

LET'S PLAY A GAME

Made in the USA
Monee, IL
03 September 2021

77220682R00085